Maths —
No Problem!

Singapore Maths
English National Curriculum 2014

Consultant
Dr. Yeap Ban Har

UK Consultant
Dr. Anne Hermanson

Author
Brandon Oh

Published by Maths — No Problem!
Copyright © 2018 by Maths — No Problem!

Printed in the United Kingdom
First Printing, 2015
Reprinted once in 2015, twice in 2016, twice in 2017
and in 2018

ISBN 978-1-910504-13-0

Maths — No Problem!
Dowding House, Coach & Horses Passage
Tunbridge Wells, UK TN2 5NP

www.mathsnoproblem.com

Acknowledgements

This Maths — No Problem! series, adapted from the New Syllabus
Primary Mathematics series, is published in collaboration with
Shing Lee Publishers. Pte Ltd. The publisher would like to thank
Dr. Tony Gardiner for his contribution.

Design and Illustration by Kin

Preface

Maths — No Problem! is a comprehensive series that adopts a spiral design with carefully built-up mathematical concepts and processes adapted from the maths mastery approaches used in Singapore. The Concrete-Pictorial-Abstract (C-P-A) approach forms an integral part of the learning process through the materials developed for this series.

Maths — No Problem! incorporates the use of concrete aids and manipulatives, problem-solving and group work.

In Maths — No Problem! Primary 4, these features are exemplified throughout the chapters:

Worksheet

Well-structured exercises which are developed in accordance with the lesson objectives of each chapter.

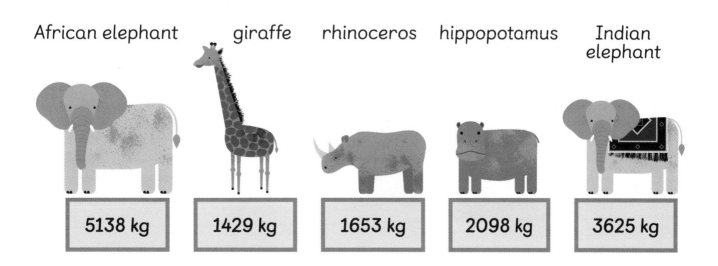

African elephant	giraffe	rhinoceros	hippopotamus	Indian elephant
5138 kg	1429 kg	1653 kg	2098 kg	3625 kg

Mind Workout

Higher-order thinking tasks as enrichment for pupils to apply relevant heuristics and extend the concepts and skills learnt.

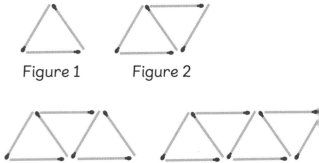

Figure 1   Figure 2

Figure 3   Figure 4

Review

Follows after each chapter for consolidation of concepts learnt in the chapter.

Bicycle
£1099

Sofa
£2150

Revision

Provides an assessment of the consolidation of concepts and skills across strands and topics.

Ring
£5988

Television
£875

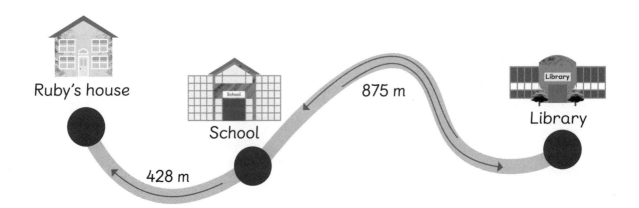

Ruby's house

School

875 m

Library

428 m

Contents

Chapter 2	Addition and Subtraction Within 10 000	Page

Chapter 3   Multiplication and Division   Page

Chapter 4   Further Multiplication and Division   Page

Chapter 7	Time	Page

Numbers to 10 000

Chapter 1

Name: _____ Class: _____ Date: _____

Worksheet 1

Counting in Hundreds and Twenty-Fives

1 Count and then write the number.

(a)

(b)

2 Complete the number patterns.

(a) 25, 50, 75, [ ] , [ ] , 150, [ ]

(b) 800, 700, 600, [ ] , [ ] , 300, [ ]

(c) [ ] , 350, 325, [ ] , 275, [ ] , 225

Name: _____ Class: _____ Date: _____

Counting in Thousands

1 Count and then write the number.

(a)  1000 1000 1000 ☐

(b) 1000 1000 1000 1000 1000 1000 1000 ☐

(c) 1000 1000 1000 1000 1000 1000 1000 1000 1000 1000 ☐

2 Complete the number patterns.

(a) 2000, 3000, ☐ , ☐ , 6000, ☐

(b) 8000, ☐ , 6000, ☐ , 4000, ☐

(c) 2000, ☐ , ☐ , ☐ , 10 000

(d) ☐ , 7000, ☐ , ☐ , 1000

Name: _____ Class: _____ Date: _____

Worksheet 3

Counting in Thousands, Hundreds, Tens and Ones

1 Count and then write the number in numerals and in words.

(a)

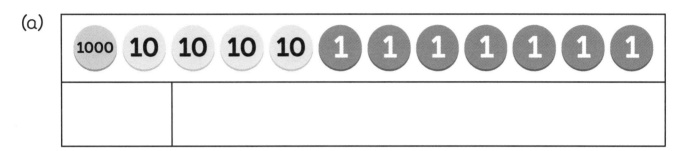

(b)

(c)

(d)

2 Complete the number patterns.

(a)   1357, 1358, 1359, ☐ , 1361, ☐

(b)   5098, ☐ , ☐ , 5101, 5102, 5103

(c)   6997, 6998, 6999, ☐ , ☐ , 7002

(d)   ☐ , 4199, 4198, 4197, 4196, ☐

(e)   ☐ , ☐ , 8998, 8997, 8996, 8995

3 Match.

five thousand, two hundred and forty-four	●	●	5424
five thousand, four hundred and twenty-four	●	●	4245
four thousand, two hundred and forty-five	●	●	5244
five thousand, two hundred and four	●	●	4240
four thousand, two hundred and fifty-four	●	●	4254
four thousand, two hundred and forty	●	●	5204

Worksheet 4

Using Place Value

1 Some number discs are shown. Sam writes the number this way:

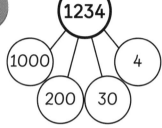

thousands	hundreds	tens	ones
1	2	3	4

1234 = [1] thousand [2] hundreds [3] tens [4] ones

1234 = [1000] + [200] + [30] + [4]

Use Sam's method to fill in the blanks.

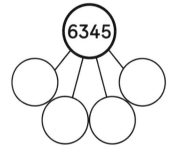

thousands	hundreds	tens	ones

6345 = [   ] thousands [   ] hundreds [   ] tens [   ] ones

6345 = [   ] + [   ] + [   ] + [   ]

2 Fill in the blanks.

(a)

4298

The digit [　] is in the thousands place.

The digit [　] is in the hundreds place.

The digit [　] is in the tens place.

The digit [　] is in the ones place.

(b)

9617

The digit 1 is in the [　] place.

The digit 9 is in the [　] place.

The digit 7 stands for [　].

The digit 9 stands for [　].

(c)

3801

The digit 8 is in the [　] place.

The digit 0 is in the [　] place.

The digit 8 stands for [　].

The digit 3 stands for [　].

Worksheet 5

Using Place Value

1 How many ways can you make a 4-digit number using these four digits?

| 2 | 2 | 7 | 7 |

	thousands	hundreds	tens	ones

	thousands	hundreds	tens	ones

	thousands	hundreds	tens	ones

	thousands	hundreds	tens	ones

	thousands	hundreds	tens	ones

	thousands	hundreds	tens	ones

2 Fill in the blanks.

	Which digit is in the hundreds place?	What does the digit 9 stand for?
4079		
4790		
9704		
7490		
7904		

Worksheet 6

Comparing and Ordering Numbers

1 Circle the greatest number.

(a)

| 127 | 214 | 476 | 543 |

(b)

| 620 | 260 | 206 | 602 |

2 Circle the smallest number.

(a)

| 304 | 460 | 639 | 503 |

(b)

| 665 | 566 | 656 | 565 |

3 Compare and write <, > or =.

(a) 234 ☐ 654   (b) 301 ☐ 103

(c) 889 ☐ 889   (d) 747 ☐ 474

4 Arrange the numbers from greatest to smallest.

| 909 | 606 | 660 | 990 |

☐ , ☐ , ☐ , ☐

Name: _____ Class: _____ Date: _____

Comparing and Ordering Numbers

1 Circle the greatest number.

(a)

| 6574 | 5873 | 6489 | 3568 |

(b)

| 3223 | 2323 | 3322 | 3232 |

2 Circle the smallest number.

(a)

| 8005 | 5600 | 7099 | 6001 |

(b)

| 2111 | 1121 | 1211 | 1112 |

3 Arrange the numbers from greatest to smallest.

5698, 3879, 2658, 6453

4 Arrange the numbers from smallest to greatest.

7797, 7779, 9777, 7977

5 Compare and then fill in the blanks.

| 3649 | 3496 |

(a) [ ] is greater than [ ] .

(b) [ ] is smaller than [ ] .

6 Compare and then fill in the blanks.

| 1221 | 3113 | 2112 | 1331 |

(a) [ ] is smaller than 1331.

(b) [ ] is the smallest.

(c) [ ] is smaller than [ ] but greater than 1331.

(d) [ ] is the greatest.

7 Form the greatest 4-digit number using the four digits given.

(a) 2, 6, 0, 8

[ ]

(b) 4, 5, 9, 3

[ ]

Name: _____ Class: _____ Date: _____

Worksheet 8

Making Number Patterns

1 Complete the table.

Number	1 more than the number	10 more than the number	100 more than the number
5938			
8999			

Number	1 less than the number	10 less than the number	100 less than the number
4818			
2791			

2 Complete the number patterns.

(a)   430, 530, [   ] , [   ] , 830, [   ]

(b)   7560, [   ] , [   ] , 7590, [   ] , 7610

3 Find the missing numbers.

(a)   1429 is [   ] more than 1419.

(b)   3299 is 1 less than [   ] .

(c)   [   ] is 100 more than 1923.

(d)   [   ] more than 5550 is 5650.

(e)   10 less than 2903 is [   ] .

Name: _____ Class: _____ Date: _____

Worksheet 9

Making Number Patterns

1 There are 1295 pupils in School A.
There are 1000 fewer pupils in School B than there are in School A.
There are 1000 more pupils in School C than there are in School A.

(a) How many pupils are there in School B?

(b) How many pupils are there in School C?

2 Complete the number patterns.

(a) [   ] , [   ] , 5025, 6025, 7025, [   ]

(b) 8989, [   ] , 6989, 5989, [   ] , [   ]

3 Find the missing numbers.

(a) 1000 more than 4938 is [   ] .

(b) 5467 is [   ] less than 6467.

(c) 6215 is 1000 more than [   ] .

(d) [   ] is 1000 less than 2871.

(e) 8627 is 1000 less than [   ] .

Name: _____ Class: _____ Date: _____

Worksheet 10

Counting in Sixes, Sevens and Nines

1 Count in sixes and circle the appropriate numbers.

1	2	3	4	5	6	7	8	9	10
11	12	13	14	15	16	17	18	19	20
21	22	23	24	25	26	27	28	29	30
31	32	33	34	35	36	37	38	39	40
41	42	43	44	45	46	47	48	49	50
51	52	53	54	55	56	57	58	59	60

2 Complete the number patterns.

(a) Counting in sevens

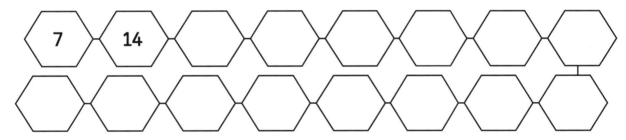

7   14

(b) Counting in nines

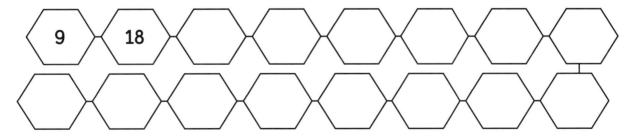

9   18

(c) Which number appears in both of the number patterns? [ ]

Name: _____ Class: _____ Date: _____

Worksheet 11

Rounding Numbers

1 The mass of some animals are shown.

(a) What is the mass of each of these animals?
Give your answers to the nearest 1000 kg.

| African elephant | giraffe | rhinoceros | hippopotamus | Indian elephant |

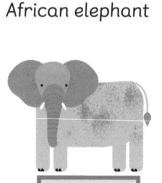  

| 5138 kg | 1429 kg | 1653 kg | 2098 kg | 3625 kg |

(b) The mass of two animals is about 2000 kg when rounded to the nearest 1000 kg.
Which two animals are they?

[   ] and [   ]

2 Round these numbers to the nearest 1000.

(a) 2278 ≈ [   ]   (b) 5499 ≈ [   ]

(c) 3501 ≈ [   ]   (d) 7684 ≈ [   ]

Name: _____ Class: _____ Date: _____

Worksheet 12

Rounding Numbers

1 The number of books in the libraries of some schools are shown.

2896 books   6257 books   3921 books   8763 books   7048 books

(a) How many books are there in the libraries of School A and School B? Give your answers to the nearest 100.

School A [   ]   School B [   ]

(b) In one school's library there are 7000 books after rounding to the nearest 1000.
Which school is that?

[   ]

(c) In one school's library the number of books is the same after rounding to the nearest 10 and to the nearest 100.
Which school is that?

[   ]

2 Complete the table.

Number	Rounding to nearest 10	Rounding to nearest 100	Rounding to nearest 1000
6543			
3751			
2033			
4545			
6004			

Name: _____ Class: _____ Date: _____

Worksheet 13

Rounding Numbers to Estimate

1 Fill in the blanks.

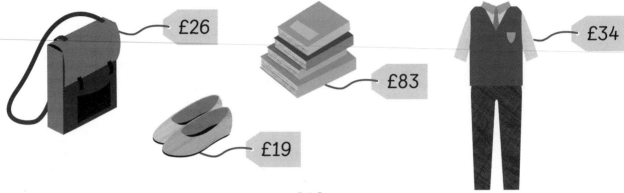

£26

£83

£34

£19

Give your answers to the nearest £10.

(a)   The cost of a school bag is about ☐ .

(b)   The cost of a pair of shoes is about ☐ .

(c)   The cost of a school uniform is about ☐ .

(d)   The cost of the textbooks is about ☐ .

(e)   The total cost of all the items is about ☐ .

2 A whole number rounded to the nearest 10 is 430.

(a)   Which whole numbers could it be?

☐

(b)   Which is the greatest of these possible numbers?   ☐

(c)   Which is the smallest of these possible numbers?   ☐

3 Sam estimates the sum of two numbers by rounding to the nearest 10.

$$52 + 37 \approx 50 + 40$$
$$= 90$$

Use Sam's method to estimate the sums below.

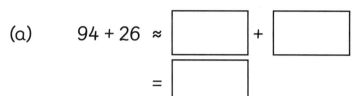

(a)   94 + 26 ≈ ⬚ + ⬚

= ⬚

(b)   123 + 81 ≈ ⬚ + ⬚

= ⬚

(c)   97 + 68 ≈ ⬚ + ⬚

= ⬚

4 Lulu estimates the difference between two numbers by rounding to the nearest 10.

$$83 - 59 \approx 80 - 60$$
$$= 20$$

Use Lulu's method to estimate the differences below.

(a)   77 - 28 ≈ ⬚ - ⬚

= ⬚

(b)   104 - 67 ≈ ⬚ - ⬚

= ⬚

(c)   683 - 496 ≈ ⬚ - ⬚

= ⬚

Name: _____ Class: _____ Date: _____

Worksheet 14

Rounding Numbers to Estimate

1 Fill in the blanks.

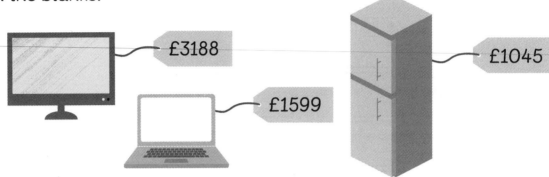

£3188

£1599

£1045

Give your answers to the nearest 100.

(a) The cost of the laptop is about [ ] .

(b) The cost of the television is about [ ] .

(c) The cost of the refrigerator is about [ ] .

(d) The total cost of all three items is about [ ] .

2 A whole number rounded to the nearest 100 is 2300.

(a) What is the greatest possible number? [ ]

(b) What is the smallest possible number? [ ]

3 A whole number rounded to the nearest 100 is 5000.

(a) What is the greatest possible number? [ ]

(b) What is the smallest possible number? [ ]

4 Ravi estimates the sum of two numbers by rounding to the nearest 100.

$$542 + 286 \approx 500 + 300$$
$$= 800$$

Use Ravi's method to estimate the sums below.

(a)   198 + 427 ≈ ☐ + ☐

= ☐

(b) 2309 + 749 ≈ ☐ + ☐

= ☐

(c) 4552 + 3106 ≈ ☐ + ☐

= ☐

5 Ruby estimates the difference between two numbers by rounding to the nearest 100.

$$624 - 359 \approx 600 - 400$$
$$= 200$$

Use Ruby's method to estimate the differences below.

(a)   865 – 251 ≈ ☐ – ☐

= ☐

(b) 3078 – 962 ≈ ☐ – ☐

= ☐

(c) 7777 – 4545 ≈ ☐ – ☐

= ☐

Date: _____

Holly and Amira were playing a card game.
They placed nine cards, numbered 1 to 9, face down on the table.
Each girl picked 3 cards and tried to form the greatest 3-digit number.
The person with the greatest 3-digit number won.

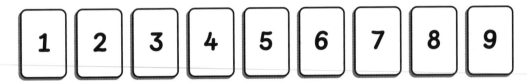

Holly picked the card with digit 7, and two other cards.

Amira picked the card with digit 9, and two other cards.

(a) What are the greatest and the smallest 3-digit numbers Holly could have formed?

[　　　] and [　　　]

(b) What are the greatest and the smallest 3-digit numbers Amira could have formed?

[　　　] and [　　　]

(c) Who do you think won the game? Explain.

[　　　　　　　　　　　　　　　　　　　　　　　　　　　]

Name: _____ Class: _____ Date: _____

Review 1

1 Count and write in numerals and in words.

(a)

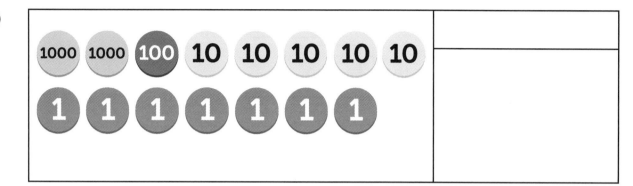

(b)

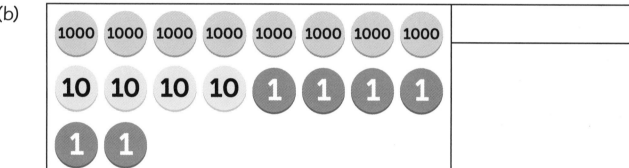

2 Arrange the numbers in order from smallest to greatest.

4567, 5764, 4657, 5467

[   ]

3 Arrange the numbers in order from greatest to smallest.

1213, 1321, 2131, 1312

[   ]

4 Find the missing numbers.

(a) 3721 is ☐ more than 2721.

(b) 6935 is ☐ less than 7035.

(c) 2078 is 100 more than ☐.

(d) 1009 is 1 less than ☐.

(e) 1000 less than 7899 is ☐.

(f) ☐ is 10 more than 4253.

(g) ☐ is 100 less than 5000.

(h) ☐ more than 990 is 1090.

5 Complete the table.

Number	Rounding to nearest 10	Rounding to nearest 100	Rounding to nearest 1000
1005			
3636			
8118			

6 Round the numbers to the nearest 100 and estimate the sum.

1647 + 2179 + 3954 ≈ ☐ + ☐ + ☐

= ☐

Addition and Subtraction Within 10 000

Chapter 2

Name: _____ Class: _____ Date: _____

Worksheet 1

Finding the Sum

1 Add.

(a) 56 + 37 = [ ]

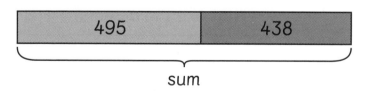

(b) 147 + 258 = [ ]

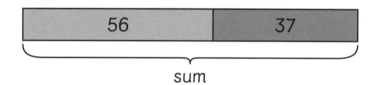

(c) 226 + 349 = [ ]

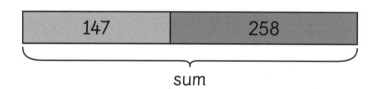

(d) 495 + 438 = [ ]

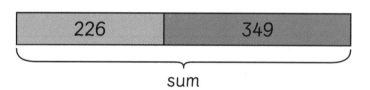

2 Fill in the blanks.

£179   £99

£375   £268

(a) The total price of the handbag and the watch is [   ].

(b) The total price of the handbag and the pair of sunglasses

is [   ].

(c) The total price of 3 pairs of shoes is [   ].

(d) Which two items together cost more than £300 but less than £400?

[   ]

(e) Emma's mother spent £742 on 3 different items.
     What are the 3 items?

[   ]

(f) The total price of all four items is [   ].

Name: _____ Class: _____ Date: _____

Worksheet 2

Adding without Renaming

1 Add.

(a)

```
    1   2   3   4
+   6   5   3   4
_____

_____
```

(b)

```
    1   7   6   5
+   4   1   3   1
_____

_____
```

(c)

```
    3   5   8   1
+   3   0   1   2
_____

_____
```

(d)

```
    4   2   2   4
+   5   5   3   3
_____

_____
```

(e)

```
    3   0   4   1
+   2   9   2   7
_____

_____
```

(f)

```
    2   2   3   5
+   7   6   4   4
_____

_____
```

2 Find the sums.

(a) 2374 + 3502 = ⬚

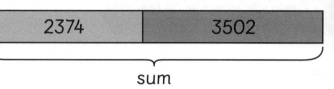

(b) 3303 + 2486 = ⬚

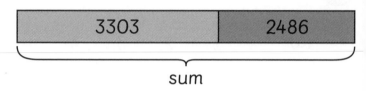

(c) 4073 + 5801 = ⬚

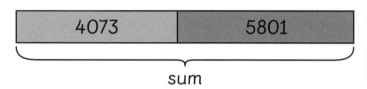

3 Circle the two numbers that give the sum.

(a)

1231 2611 4400 3002	Sum
	5613

(b)

3085 1704 3084 1706	Sum
	4789

Worksheet 3

Adding with Renaming

1 Add.

(a)
```
    1   3   2   5
+   1   6   3   5
_____

_____
```

(b)
```
    2   4   7   6
+   1   4   1   5
_____

_____
```

(c)
```
    3   2   3   7
+   4   5   2   8
_____

_____
```

(d)
```
    4   1   6   9
+   2   7   0   4
_____

_____
```

(e)
```
    3   4   2   8
+   1   2   1   8
_____

_____
```

(f)
```
    1   2   3   9
+   8   2   0   3
_____

_____
```

(g)
```
    1   6   3   5
+   4   2   3   9
_____

_____
```

(h)
```
    7   2   7   6
+   2   3   1   4
_____

_____
```

2 Find the sums.

(a)   634 + 1238 = ⬜

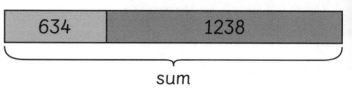

sum

(b)   2453 + 2539 = ⬜

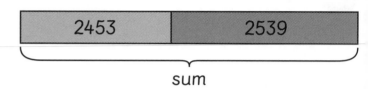

sum

(c)   6075 + 2308 = ⬜

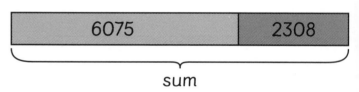

sum

3 Circle the two numbers that give the sum.

(a)

3506 6205 1429 4137	Sum
	7634

(b)

7028 2241 6103 1438	Sum
	8466

Worksheet 4

Adding with Renaming

1 Add.

(a)
```
    2  1  7  6
+   2  3  4  6
_____
```

(b)
```
    1  0  5  3
+   4  6  8  8
_____
```

(c)
```
    2  2  5  8
+   5  1  6  7
_____
```

(d)
```
    3  1  4  6
+   3  7  5  7
_____
```

(e)
```
    1  4  6  3
+   8  3  3  7
_____
```

(f)
```
    7  2  2  9
+   2  2  8  9
_____
```

(g)
```
    5  2  9  4
+   3  1  1  7
_____
```

(h)
```
    2  6  4  8
+   4  2  5  8
_____
```

2 Find the sums.

(a)　748 + 1153 = ☐

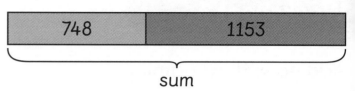

sum

(b)　3345 + 2477 = ☐

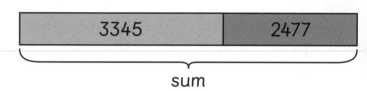

sum

(c)　5039 + 2468 = ☐

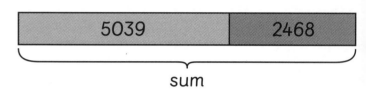

sum

3 Match the two numbers that give the sum 4800.

● [**3556**]

[**1454**] ●

● [**3566**]

[**1234**] ●

● [**3346**]

Worksheet 5

Adding with Renaming

1 Add.

(a)
```
    1  4  5  2
 +  1  7  6  9
 _____
```

(b)
```
    1  7  4  6
 +  2  6  8  4
 _____
```

(c)
```
    2  9  8  6
 +  3  0  5  8
 _____
```

(d)
```
    3  7  4  5
 +  1  4  6  7
 _____
```

(e)
```
    3  3  5  4
 +  4  8  5  7
 _____
```

(f)
```
    5  7  6  6
 +  3  3  7  5
 _____
```

(g)
```
    2  6  7  8
 +  4  3  8  9
 _____
```

(h)
```
    2  5  7  9
 +  2  7  3  5
 _____
```

2 Find the sums.

(a) $839 + 1476 =$ ⬜

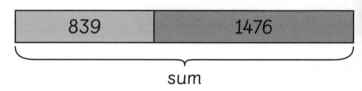

sum

(b) $2733 + 3677 =$ ⬜

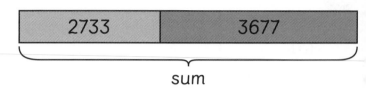

sum

(c) $4186 + 3827 =$ ⬜

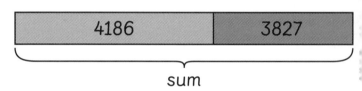

sum

3 Match the two numbers that give the sum 8000.

● 2625

5375 ●

● 2635

5465 ●

● 2535

Worksheet 6

Adding Using Mental Strategies

Add mentally and fill in the blanks.

(a) $1871 + 9 =$ [ ] $+ 10 =$ [ ]

(b) $2998 + 52 =$ [ ] $+$ [ ] $=$ [ ]

(c) $5998 + 1112 =$ [ ] $+$ [ ] $=$ [ ]

(d) $82 + 1999 =$ [ ] $+$ [ ] $=$ [ ]

(e) $2222 + 3999 =$ [ ] $+$ [ ] $=$ [ ]

(f) $4999 + 388 =$ [ ] $+$ [ ] $=$ [ ]

(g) $398 + 1295 =$ [ ] $+$ [ ] $=$ [ ]

Worksheet 7

Adding Using Mental Strategies

1 Add mentally and fill in the blanks.

(a) Find the sum of 297 and 6998.

300	+	7000	=	

297 + 6998 = [ ] − [ ] = [ ]

(b) Find the sum of 5713 and 3998.

[ ] + [ ] = [ ]

5713 + 3998 = [ ] − [ ] = [ ]

(c) Find the sum of 4899 and 2997.

[ ] + [ ] = [ ]

4899 + 2997 = [ ] − [ ] = [ ]

2 Add mentally and match.

| 4799 + 1299 | ● |
| 1999 + 3599 | ● |

● 6098

● 5598

● 6005

Name: _____ Class: _____ Date: _____

Worksheet 8

Finding Differences

1 Find the difference.

(a)

225 kg   34 kg

The difference is [ ] kg.

(b)

248   310

Box A   Box B

The difference is [ ] apples.

2 Find the difference.

(a)

735 ml

350 ml

The difference is [ ] ml.

(b)

£83

£238

The difference is £ [ ].

Worksheet 9

Subtracting without Renaming

1 Subtract.

(a)
```
    2  1  3  4
  - 1  1  2  3
  _____

  _____
```

(b)
```
    3  7  3  6
  - 1  4  3  5
  _____

  _____
```

(c)
```
    5  8  8  9
  - 3  2  4  7
  _____

  _____
```

(d)
```
    6  6  9  4
  - 3  4  5  4
  _____

  _____
```

(e)
```
    7  3  9  9
  - 1  0  2  7
  _____

  _____
```

(f)
```
    8  6  9  7
  - 6  4  5  3
  _____

  _____
```

2 Find the difference.

(a) $4783 - 2552 =$ ⬚

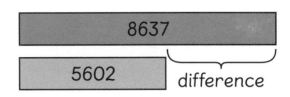

(b) $8637 - 5602 =$ ⬚

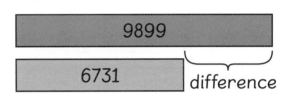

(c) $9899 - 6731 =$ ⬚

3 Circle the two numbers that give the difference.

(a)

8899 1200 1300 8999	Difference
	7799

(b)

4365 3743 2262 1630	Difference
	2113

Worksheet 10

Subtracting with Renaming

1 Subtract.

(a) 1453 − 227 = ☐

```
      1   4   5   3
  -       2   2   7
  _____
```

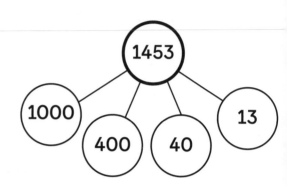

(b) 2657 − 1248 = ☐

```
      2   6   5   7
  -   1   2   4   8
  _____
```

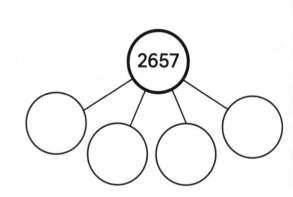

(c) 6842 − 4128 = ☐

```
      6   8   4   2
  -   4   1   2   8
  _____
```

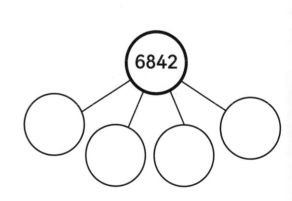

2 Subtract.

(a)
```
    1  8  5  5
 -  1  2  3  6
 _____

 _____
```

(b)
```
    2  9  7  1
 -  1  4  2  8
 _____

 _____
```

(c)
```
    3  6  3  7
 -  1  4  2  8
 _____

 _____
```

(d)
```
    5  8  7  3
 -  2  2  3  7
 _____

 _____
```

(e)
```
    5  7  9  7
 -  1  3  3  9
 _____

 _____
```

(f)
```
    8  5  8  3
 -  1  5  3  9
 _____

 _____
```

(g)
```
    7  8  6  5
 -  2  2  3  7
 _____

 _____
```

(h)
```
    9  3  5  2
 -  4  3  3  9
 _____

 _____
```

Worksheet 11

Subtracting with Renaming

Subtract.

1 65 – 38 = 75 – [48]

= [ ]

2 315 – 167 = 425 – [ ]

= [ ]

3 2654 – 1738 = 3664 – [ ]

= [ ]

4 7458 – 4689 = 8568 – [ ]

= [ ]

```
          [ ]
      6    5
  –   3    8
     [ ]
  _____
```

```
     [ ]  [ ]
  3   1    5
– 1   6    7
  [ ] [ ]
  _____
```

```
     [ ]      [ ]
2    6    5    4
– 1  7    3    8
[ ]      [ ]
  _____
```

```
     [ ]  [ ]  [ ]
7    4    5    8
– 4  6    8    9
[ ]  [ ]  [ ]
  _____
```

Worksheet 12

Subtracting with Renaming

1 Subtract.

(a)   5723 – 79 = ⬚

⬚ ⬚ ⬚

    5   7   2   3
–   7   9
―――――――――――――

―――――――――――――

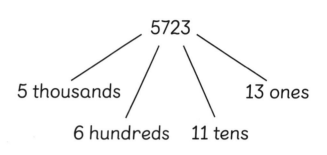

5723
5 thousands   13 ones
6 hundreds   11 tens

(b)   3593 – 496 = ⬚

⬚ ⬚ ⬚

    3   5   9   3
–   4   9   6
―――――――――――――

―――――――――――――

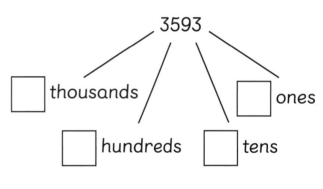

3593
⬚ thousands   ⬚ ones
⬚ hundreds   ⬚ tens

(c)   7925 – 3688 = ⬚

⬚ ⬚ ⬚

    7   9   2   5
–   3   6   8   8
―――――――――――――

―――――――――――――

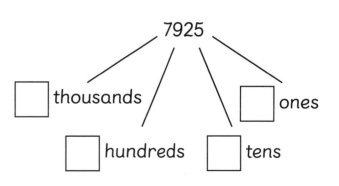

7925
⬚ thousands   ⬚ ones
⬚ hundreds   ⬚ tens

2 Subtract.

(a)
```
    3  6  1  7
 -  2  3  2  8
_____

_____
```

(b)
```
    5  4  8  7
 -  1  3  9  9
_____

_____
```

(c)
```
    6  8  4  2
 -  3  2  9  8
_____

_____
```

(d)
```
    7  9  2  1
 -  2  3  4  8
_____

_____
```

(e)
```
    7  6  2  4
 -  4  3  3  9
_____

_____
```

(f)
```
    8  5  0  2
 -  3  2  0  5
_____

_____
```

(g)
```
    8  7  3  4
 -  5  2  6  7
_____

_____
```

(h)
```
    9  9  1  1
 -  1  1  9  9
_____

_____
```

Worksheet 13

Subtracting with Renaming

1 This is how Ruby finds the difference between 3000 and 1758.

$3000 - 1758 =$ ☐ 1242

$3000 - 1000 = 2000$

$2000 - 700 = 1300$

$1300 - 50 = 1250$

$1250 - 8 = 1242$

Use Ruby's method to fill in the blanks.

(a) $6000 - 3769 =$ ☐ $6000 - 3000 =$ ☐

☐ $- 700 =$ ☐

☐ $- 60 =$ ☐

☐ $- 9 =$ ☐

(b) $7003 - 2814 =$ ☐ $7003 - 2000 =$ ☐

☐ $-$ ☐ $=$ ☐

☐ $-$ ☐ $=$ ☐

☐ $-$ ☐ $=$ ☐

2 This is Elliott's method of finding the difference between 5000 and 2487.

5000 − 2487 = ┌─────┐
               │ ? │
               └─────┘

5000 − 2487 = ┌─────┐
               │ 2513│
               └─────┘

4999 − 2487 = 2512

2512 + 1 = ┌──────┐
           │ 2513 │
           └──────┘

Find the difference using Elliott's method.

(a)   4000 − 2965 = ┌─────┐   ┌─────┐ − ┌─────┐ = ┌─────┐
                     │   │   │   │   │   │   │   │
                     └─────┘   └─────┘   └─────┘   └─────┘

                                  ┌─────┐ + ┌─────┐ = ┌─────┐
                                  │   │   │   │   │   │
                                  └─────┘   └─────┘   └─────┘

(b)   9002 − 7789 = ┌─────┐   ┌─────┐ − ┌─────┐ = ┌─────┐
                     │   │   │   │   │   │   │   │
                     └─────┘   └─────┘   └─────┘   └─────┘

                                  ┌─────┐ + ┌─────┐ = ┌─────┐
                                  │   │   │   │   │   │
                                  └─────┘   └─────┘   └─────┘

3 Subtract.

(a)   6 0 0 0   (b)   5 1 0 0
      − 2 6 8 4   −   1 8 5 3
      ─────────────────   ─────────────────

      ─────────────────   ─────────────────

(c)   4 0 8 0   (d)   7 0 0 1
      − 1 6 8 7   −   3 4 5 6
      ─────────────────   ─────────────────

      ─────────────────   ─────────────────

Name: _____ Class: _____ Date: _____

Worksheet 14

Subtracting Using Mental Strategies

1 Amira finds the difference between 4995 and 1856 this way.

4995 − 1856 = [?]

4996 − 1856 = 3140

3140 − 1   = [3139]

```
    4   9   9   6
−   1   8   5   6
───────────────
    3   1   4   0
───────────────
```

Use Amira's method to subtract the following.

(a)   5863 − 4235 = [   ]

[   ] − 4235 = [   ]

[   ] − 2   = [   ]

```
[  ] [  ] [  ] [  ]
−   4   2   3   5
───────────────


───────────────
```

(b)   6952 − 1387 = [   ]

[   ] − 1387 = [   ]

[   ] − [   ] = [   ]

```
[  ] [  ] [  ] [  ]
−   1   3   8   7
───────────────


───────────────
```

2 Ravi finds the difference between 1996 and 2005 this way.

2005 – 1996 = [?]

2000 – 1996 = 4

2005 – 2000 = 5

4 + 5 = [9]

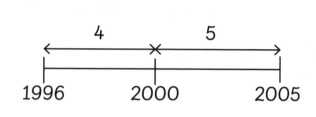

4   5

1996   2000   2005

Use Ravi's method to subtract the following.

(a)   6095 – 5997 = [   ]

[   ] – [   ] = [   ]

[   ] – [   ] = [   ]

[   ] + [   ] = [   ]

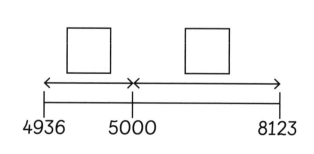

5997   6000   6095

(b)   8123 – 4936 = [   ]

[   ] – [   ] = [   ]

[   ] – [   ] = [   ]

[   ] + [   ] = [   ]

4936   5000   8123

Name: _____ Class: _____ Date: _____

Worksheet 15

Solving Word Problems

Solve.

1 There are 283 boys and 327 girls in the hall.
195 children leave the hall.
How many pupils are left in the hall?

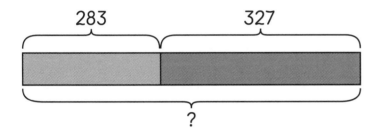

283   327

?

[ ] ◯ [ ] = [ ]

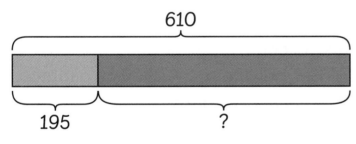

610

195   ?

[ ] ◯ [ ] = [ ]

There are [ ] pupils left in the hall.

2 There are 8265 books in a school library.
2678 are fiction books and 4679 are non-fiction books.
The rest are reference books.
How many reference books are there in the library?

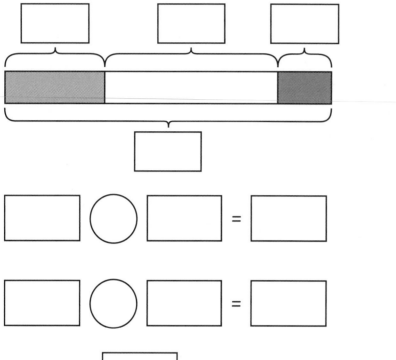

There are [ ] reference books in the library.

3 Hannah had £2327 in her savings account.
This month she saved another £1096, but she spent £999 on a laptop.
How much money does she have left in her account?

Name: _____ Class: _____ Date: _____

Worksheet 16

Solving Word Problems

Solve.

1 A baker baked 2568 chocolate buns.
He baked 853 fewer cheese buns than chocolate buns.
How many buns did he bake altogether?

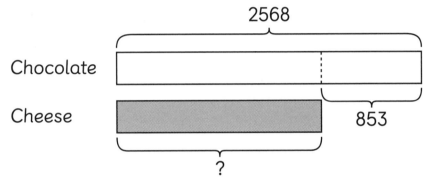

He baked [ ] cheese buns.

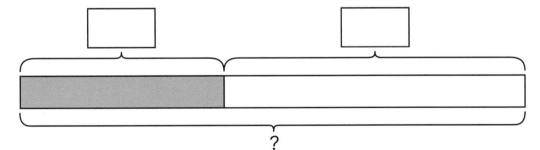

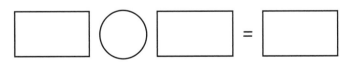

He baked [ ] buns altogether.

2 4824 people visited the museum on Tuesday.
1879 more people visited the museum on Tuesday than visited on Monday.
How many people visited the museum over the two days?

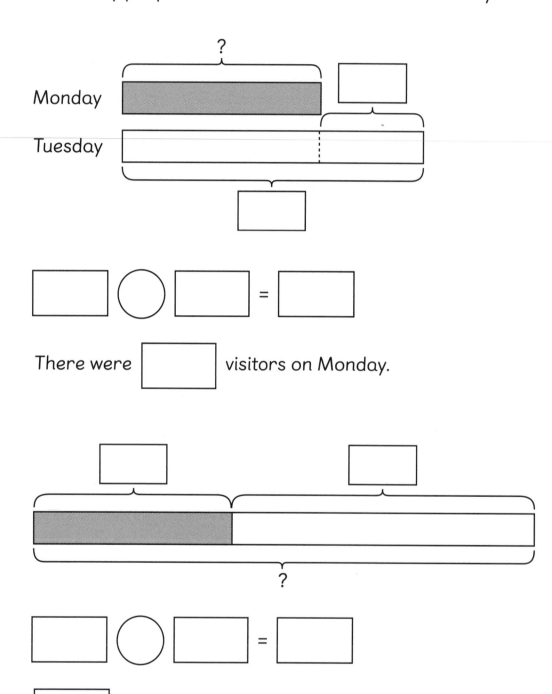

Monday

Tuesday

There were [ ] visitors on Monday.

[ ] ◯ [ ] = [ ]

[ ] people visited the museum over the two days.

Worksheet 17

Solving Word Problems

Solve.

1 Emma has 294 more stickers than Lulu has.
If Emma gives 120 stickers to Lulu, who will have more stickers?
How many more stickers will she have?

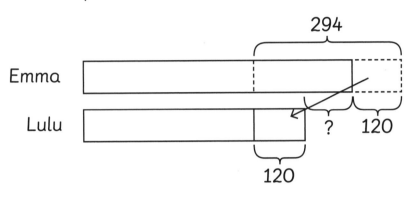

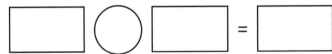

[   ] has more stickers. She has [   ] more.

2 Sam had £463 more than Charles.

Charles then gave £246 to Sam.

How much more money did Sam have than Charles in the end?

3 There was 2438 ml of water in a container.

There was 3987 ml of water in a bucket.

805 ml of water from the bucket was poured into the container.

Which of the two has more water now?

How much more?

4 Box A and Box B had some coins inside them.
Amira moved 293 coins from Box A into Box B.
Box B then had 501 more coins in it than Box A had.
Which box had more coins at first? How many more?

Sam is using a calculator to find the difference between two numbers.

$$8000 - 3807 = \text{?}$$

However, the zero button on the calculator is faulty.
Suggest two ways he can find the answer without using the zero button.
Explain your answer.

Oh no...
I can't key in
the digit '0'...

Review 2

1 Fill in the blanks.

Bicycle
£1099

Sofa
£2150

Ring
£5988

Television
£875

(a) The total cost of the ring and the sofa is ⬚ .

(b) The difference in price between the bicycle and the

sofa is ⬚ .

(c) The total cost of 2 bicycles is ⬚ .

(d) Which three items together cost more than £7000 but less than £8000 in total?

⬚

(e) Which two items have the smallest price difference? What is the difference?

⬚

2 Add or subtract.

(a)
```
    3   4   6   6
+   2   5   1   2
_____

_____
```

(b)
```
    5   4   7   5
+   2   3   8   5
_____

_____
```

(c)
```
    3   6   8   5
+   5   6   4   8
_____

_____
```

(d)
```
    2   9   6   8
+   6   0   8   9
_____

_____
```

(e)
```
    5   8   4   5
-   2   5   1   8
_____

_____
```

(f)
```
    6   6   2   3
-   5   2   3   9
_____

_____
```

(g)
```
    7   4   8   6
-   4   5   8   9
_____

_____
```

(h)
```
    8   0   3   8
-   2   5   3   9
_____

_____
```

Solve.

3 A bakery baked 2352 chocolate biscuits and 1203 vanilla biscuits.
They sold 1897 biscuits.
How many biscuits did they have left?

4 There are 2107 pupils in School A.
There are 587 fewer pupils in School A than there are in School B.
How many pupils are there in School A and School B altogether?

Multiplication and Division

Name: _____ Class: _____ Date: _____

Worksheet 1

Multiplying by 6

1 Multiply by counting in sixes.

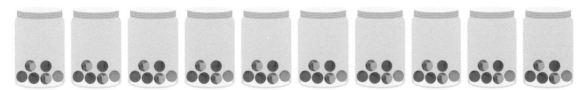

(a) $3 × 6 = $ ☐

(b) $6 × 6 = $ ☐

(c) $5 × 6 = $ ☐

(d) $2 × 6 = $ ☐

(e) $8 × 6 = $ ☐

(f) $10 × 6 = $ ☐

(g) $7 × 6 = $ ☐

(h) $9 × 6 = $ ☐

2 Write down two multiplication statements.

☐ × ☐ = ☐   ☐ × ☐ = ☐

3 Complete the number patterns.

(a)　6, 12, 18, 24, ▢ , ▢

(b)　24, 30, ▢ , ▢ , 48

(c)　36, ▢ , 48, ▢ , 60

(d)　▢ , ▢ , 24, 30, 36

4 Match.

9 × 6	●		●	42
6 × 6	●		●	54
5 × 6	●		●	36
8 × 6	●		●	48
7 × 6	●		●	30

5 Fill in the blanks.

(a)　6 + 6 + 6 + 6 + 6 + 6 + 6 + 6 = ▢ × 6

(b)　4 × 6 = ▢ + ▢ + ▢ + ▢

Worksheet 2

Multiplying by 7

1 Fill in the blanks.

$3 \times 7 = 21$

$4 \times 7 = 21 +$ ☐ $=$ ☐

2 Complete the number patterns.

(a)   7, 14, 21, ☐ , ☐ , 42

(b)   35, ☐ , 49, ☐ , 63

(c)   ☐ , ☐ , 56, 63, 70

3 Match.

7 × 7	•		•	21
3 × 7	•		•	63
4 × 7	•		•	56
9 × 7	•		•	49
6 × 7	•		•	28
8 × 7	•		•	42

Worksheet 3

Multiplying by 9

1 Multiply by counting in nines.

(a) $5 \times 9 = $ ☐

(b) $3 \times 9 = $ ☐

(c) $2 \times 9 = $ ☐

(d) $4 \times 9 = $ ☐

(e) $7 \times 9 = $ ☐

(f) $6 \times 9 = $ ☐

(g) $10 \times 9 = $ ☐

(h) $9 \times 9 = $ ☐

2 Fill in the blanks.

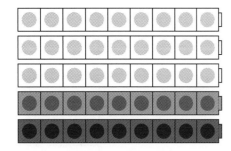

$3 \times 9 = 27$

$4 \times 9 = 27 + $ ☐ $ = $ ☐

$5 \times 9 = $ ☐ $ + $ ☐ $ = $ ☐

3 Complete the number patterns.

(a) 9, 18, 27, [   ] , [   ] , 54

(b) 27, [   ] , 45, [   ] , 63

(c) [   ] , [   ] , 45, 54, 63

(d) 45, 54, 63, [   ] , [   ] , 90

(e) [   ] , 18, 27, 36, 45, [   ]

4 Match.

7 × 9	●		●	27
3 × 9	●		●	63
4 × 9	●		●	81
2 × 9	●		●	36
5 × 9	●		●	18
9 × 9	●		●	72
6 × 9	●		●	54
8 × 9	●		●	45

Worksheet 4

Multiplying by 9

1 Fill in the blanks.

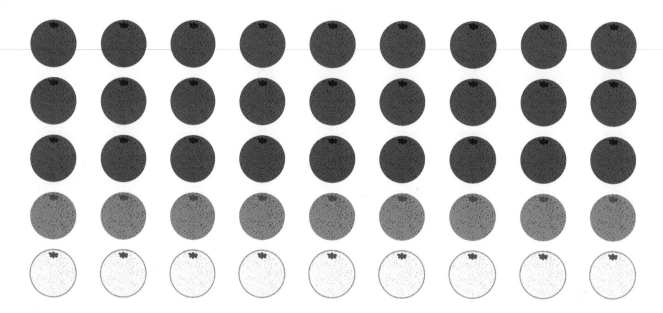

$5 \times 9 = 45$

$4 \times 9 = 45 - \boxed{} = \boxed{}$

$3 \times 9 = \boxed{} - \boxed{} = \boxed{}$

2 Write the missing numbers.

(a)   5 × 9 = [   ]

4 × 9 = [   ]

3 × 9 = [   ]

2 × 9 = [   ]

1 × 9 = [   ]

(b)   10 × 9 = [   ]

9 × 9 = [   ]

8 × 9 = [   ]

7 × 9 = [   ]

6 × 9 = [   ]

Worksheet 5

Multiplying by 11

1 Fill in the blanks.

$1 \times 11 = $ [ ] $6 \times 11 = $ [ ]

$2 \times 11 = $ [ ] $7 \times 11 = $ [ ]

$3 \times 11 = $ [ ] $8 \times 11 = $ [ ]

$4 \times 11 = $ [ ] $9 \times 11 = $ [ ]

$5 \times 11 = $ [ ] $10 \times 11 = $ [ ]

2 Fill in the blanks.

(a) $4 \times 11 = $ [ ] $+$ [ ] $=$ [ ]

(b) $8 \times 11 = 4 \times 11 + 4 \times 11$

$= $ [ ] $+$ [ ] $=$ [ ]

(c) $8 \times 11 = $ [ ] $\times 10 + $ [ ] $\times 1$

$= $ [ ] $+$ [ ] $=$ [ ]

Worksheet 6

Multiplying by 11

 1 Fill in the blanks.

$6 \times 11 = 66$
$11 \times 9 = 99$

(a) $6 \times 11 =$ ☐ $\times 6 =$ ☐

(b) $11 \times 9 =$ ☐ $\times 11 =$ ☐

(c) $7 \times 11 =$ ☐ $+$ ☐ $=$ ☐

(d) $5 \times 11 =$ ☐ $-$ ☐ $=$ ☐

(e) $11 \times 10 =$ ☐ $+$ ☐ $=$ ☐

(f) $11 \times 8 =$ ☐ $-$ ☐ $=$ ☐

(g) $12 \times 11 = 6 \times 11 +$ ☐ $\times 11$

   $=$ ☐ $+$ ☐ $=$ ☐

Worksheet 7

Multiplying by 12

1 Fill in the blanks.

12	12	12	12	12	12
12	12	12	12	12	12

(a) $2 \times 12 = $ ☐ $+$ ☐ $=$ ☐

(b) $3 \times 12 = $ ☐ $+$ ☐ $=$ ☐

(c) $4 \times 12 = $ ☐ $+$ ☐ $=$ ☐

(d) $6 \times 12 = $ ☐ $+$ ☐ $=$ ☐

(e) $5 \times 12 = $ ☐ $+$ ☐ $=$ ☐

(f) $7 \times 12 = $ ☐ $+$ ☐ $=$ ☐

(g) $10 \times 12 = $ ☐ $+$ ☐ $=$ ☐

(h) $8 \times 12 = $ ☐ $+$ ☐ $=$ ☐

(i) $9 \times 12 = $ ☐ $+$ ☐ $=$ ☐

2 Fill in the blanks.

10 × 12 = 120
2 × 12 = 24

(a) 10 × 12 = [ ] × 10 = [ ]

(b) 2 × 12 = 12 × [ ] = [ ]

(c) 11 × 12 = [ ] + [ ] = [ ]

(d) 9 × 12 = [ ] - [ ] = [ ]

(e) 12 × 12 = [ ] + [ ] = [ ]

(f) 12 × 11 = [ ] - [ ] = [ ]

(g) 8 × 12 = 10 × 12 - [ ] × 12

= [ ] - [ ] = [ ]

Worksheet 8

Dividing by 6

1 Circle the items to make groups of 6 and write down the division equations.

(a)

$$\boxed{} \div \boxed{} = \boxed{}$$

There are $\boxed{}$ equal groups.

(b)

$$\boxed{} \div \boxed{} = \boxed{}$$

There are $\boxed{}$ equal groups.

2 Circle the items to make 6 equal groups and write down the division equations.

(a)

[　　　] ÷ [　　　] = [　　　]

There are [　　　] cupcakes in each group.

(b)

[　　　] ÷ [　　　] = [　　　]

There are [　　　] marbles in each group.

3 Write the missing numbers.

(a) $\boxed{} \times 6 = 24$

$24 \div 6 = \boxed{}$

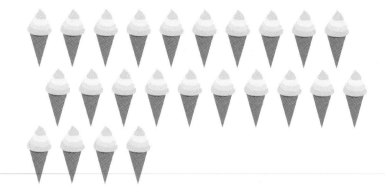

(b) $\boxed{} \times 6 = 36$

$36 \div 6 = \boxed{}$

(c) $6 \times \boxed{} = 48$

$48 \div 6 = \boxed{}$

(d) $\boxed{} \times 6 = 60$

$60 \div 6 = \boxed{}$

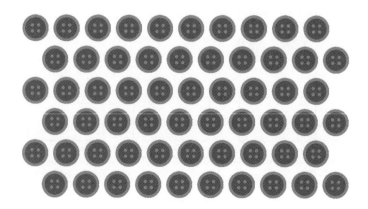

Name: _____ Class: _____ Date: _____

Worksheet 9

Dividing by 7

1 Circle the items to make groups of 7 and write down the division equations.

(a)

[   ] ÷ [   ] = [   ]

There are [   ] equal groups.

(b)

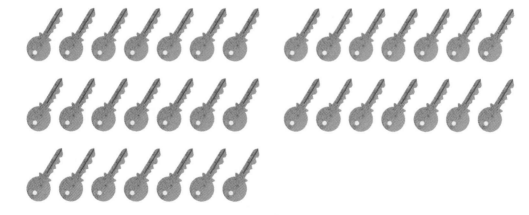

[   ] ÷ [   ] = [   ]

There are [   ] equal groups.

2 Circle the items to make 7 equal groups and write down the division equations.

(a)

$$\boxed{} \div \boxed{} = \boxed{}$$

There are $\boxed{}$ oranges in each group.

(b)

$$\boxed{} \div \boxed{} = \boxed{}$$

There are $\boxed{}$ matchsticks in each group.

3 Write the missing numbers.

(a)
$$\boxed{} \times 7 = 21$$

$$21 \div 7 = \boxed{}$$

(b)
$$\boxed{} \times 7 = 28$$

$$28 \div 7 = \boxed{}$$

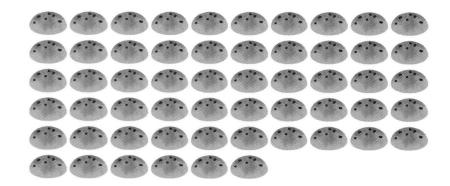

(c)
$$7 \times \boxed{} = 56$$

$$56 \div 7 = \boxed{}$$

(d)
$$\boxed{} \times 7 = 63$$

$$63 \div 7 = \boxed{}$$

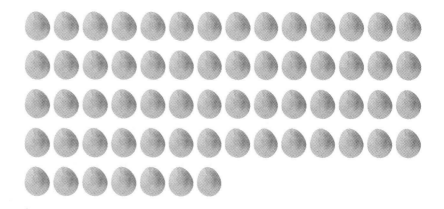

Worksheet 10

Dividing by 9

1 Circle the items to make groups of 9 and write down the division equations.

(a)

$$\boxed{} \div \boxed{} = \boxed{}$$

There are $\boxed{}$ equal groups.

(b)

$$\boxed{} \div \boxed{} = \boxed{}$$

There are $\boxed{}$ equal groups.

2 Circle the items to make 9 equal groups and write down the division equations.

(a)

$\boxed{} \div \boxed{} = \boxed{}$

There are $\boxed{}$ pencils in each group.

(b)

$\boxed{} \div \boxed{} = \boxed{}$

There are $\boxed{}$ strawberries in each group.

3 Write the missing numbers.

(a) $\boxed{} \times 9 = 36$

$36 \div 9 = \boxed{}$

(b) $\boxed{} \times 9 = 81$

$81 \div 9 = \boxed{}$

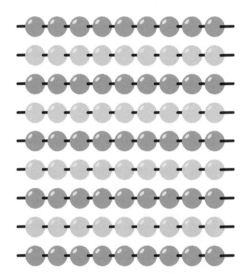

4 Write down the quotients.

(a)   54 divided by 9   quotient $\boxed{}$

(b)   36 divided by 9   quotient $\boxed{}$

(c)   90 divided by 9   quotient $\boxed{}$

(d)   63 divided by 9   quotient $\boxed{}$

Worksheet 11

Multiplying and Dividing by 11 and 12

1 Write a family of multiplication and division facts based on the pictures.

(a)

3	×	11	=				÷		=	

	×		=				÷		=	

(b)

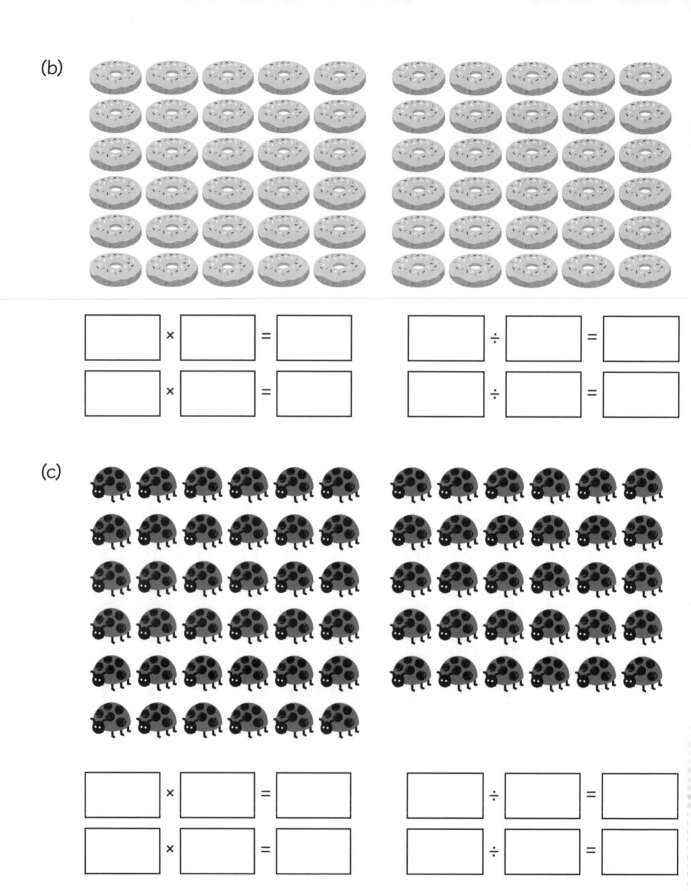

| | × | | = | |
| | × | | = | |

| | ÷ | | = | |
| | ÷ | | = | |

(c)

| | × | | = | |
| | × | | = | |

| | ÷ | | = | |
| | ÷ | | = | |

2 Fill in the blanks.

(a)

| 12 | 12 | 12 | 12 | 12 | 12 | 12 |

$\boxed{} \times 12 = \boxed{}$

$\boxed{} \div 12 = \boxed{}$

$\boxed{} \div \boxed{} = 12$

(b)

| 11 | 11 | 11 | 11 | 11 |
| 11 | 11 | 11 | 11 | 11 |

$11 \times \boxed{} = \boxed{}$

$\boxed{} \div 11 = \boxed{}$

$\boxed{} \div \boxed{} = 11$

3 Fill in the blanks.

(a) $12 \times 11 = \boxed{}$

(b) $132 \div 11 = \boxed{}$

(c) $132 \div 12 = \boxed{}$

(d) $11 \times 11 = \boxed{}$

$11 \times 12 = 132$

Worksheet 12

Dividing with Remainder

1 Circle the objects and fill in the blanks.

(a)   Circle the watermelons to make groups of 5.

$$\boxed{} \div \boxed{} = \boxed{} \text{ remainder } \boxed{}$$

(b)   Circle the tarts to make groups of 6.

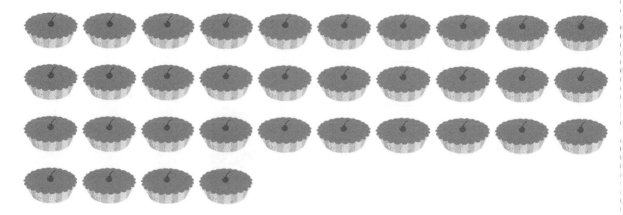

$$\boxed{} \div \boxed{} = \boxed{} \text{ remainder } \boxed{}$$

(c) Circle the birds to make groups of 9.

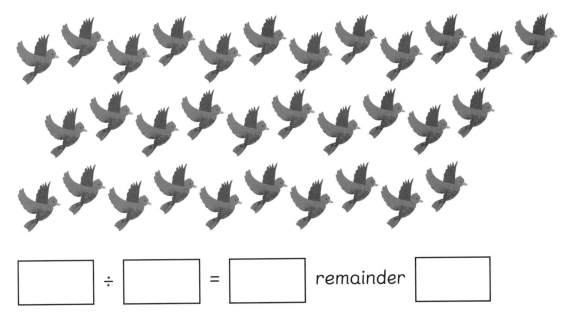

$\boxed{} \div \boxed{} = \boxed{}$ remainder $\boxed{}$

2 Holly has 37 stickers.
She pastes them equally onto 7 cards.

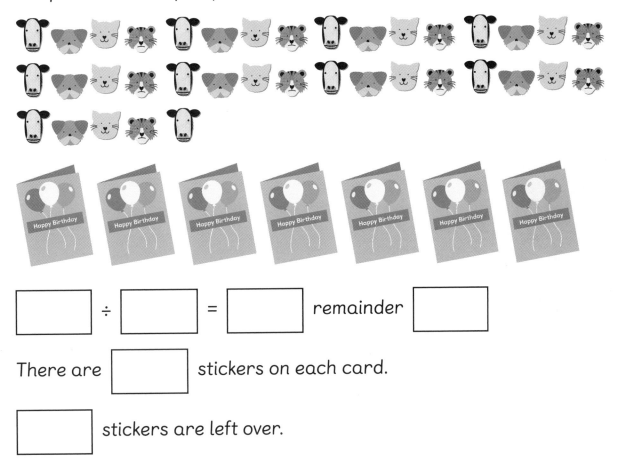

$\boxed{} \div \boxed{} = \boxed{}$ remainder $\boxed{}$

There are $\boxed{}$ stickers on each card.

$\boxed{}$ stickers are left over.

3 Ravi wants to put 74 basketballs into baskets.
Each basket can hold 8 basketballs.

☐ ÷ ☐ = ☐ remainder ☐

Ravi needs at least ☐ baskets.

4 Ruby wants to spend £50 on some T-shirts.

£6

☐ ÷ ☐ = ☐ remainder ☐

The most T-shirts Ruby can buy is ☐ .

Name: _____ Class: _____ Date: _____

Worksheet 13

Solving Word Problems

Solve.

1 At a bakery, cupcakes are sold in small boxes or large boxes.

(a) Amira bought 6 large boxes and 4 small boxes of cupcakes for her family party.
How many cupcakes did she buy altogether?

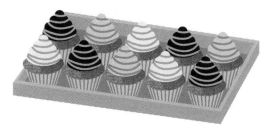

☐ × ☐ = ☐		
☐ × ☐ = ☐		
☐ + ☐ = ☐		

Amira bought ☐ cupcakes altogether.

(b) Back at home, Amira put all the cupcakes she bought onto trays.
There were 10 cupcakes on each tray.
How many trays did she use?

☐ ÷ ☐ = ☐

Amira used ☐ trays.

2 Hannah brought 3 boxes of chocolate cookies to school to share with her friends.

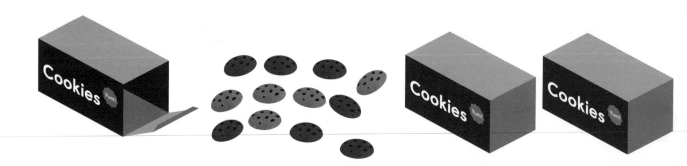

(a) There were 12 cookies in each box.
Hannah shared all the cookies with her friends.
Each of them received 6 cookies.
How many friends did Hannah share her cookies with?

$$\boxed{} \times \boxed{} = \boxed{}$$

$$\boxed{} \div \boxed{} = \boxed{}$$

$$\boxed{} - \boxed{} = \boxed{}$$

Hannah shared her cookies with $\boxed{}$ friends.

(b) If Hannah shared the cookies with 8 friends instead, how many cookies would each person receive?

$$\boxed{} + \boxed{} = \boxed{}$$

$$\boxed{} \div \boxed{} = \boxed{}$$

Each person would receive $\boxed{}$ cookies.

Name: _____ Class: _____ Date: _____

Worksheet 14

Solving Word Problems

Solve.

1 Elliott takes some square tiles from a box to form a square.
He wants to make a square that has 6 rows with 6 square tiles in each row.
However, Elliott can only form 4 rows of 6 square tiles.

(a)   How many more square tiles does he need to form the square?

	×		=	

He needs [   ] more square tiles.

(b)   Elliott takes 30 more square tiles from the box.
Now he wants to form a square with all the tiles.
After forming the largest square he can, how many square tiles are
left over?

$\boxed{}$ × $\boxed{}$ = $\boxed{}$

$\boxed{}$ + $\boxed{}$ = $\boxed{}$

$\boxed{}$ × $\boxed{}$ = $\boxed{}$

$\boxed{}$ - $\boxed{}$ = $\boxed{}$

$\boxed{}$ square tiles are left over.

Worksheet 15

Solving Word Problems

Fill in the blanks.

Mr Pizza

Pepperoni Pizza	£12
Chicken Pizza	£9
Mushroom Pizza	£7
Extra Topping	£2

1 Find the cost of the pizzas.

(a) Emma's pizzas cost  .

I want four mushroom pizzas with one extra topping on each.

(b)   Charles' pizzas cost [   ] .

I want two pepperoni pizzas and three chicken pizzas, all without extra toppings.

(c)   Lulu's pizzas cost [   ] .

I want five mushroom pizzas without extra toppings and one pepperoni pizza with an extra topping.

(d)   The three groups of pizzas cost [   ] in total.

2 Sam wants to buy at least 75 fruit tarts for a party with his friends.

How much does Sam need to pay?

☐ ÷ ☐ = ☐ remainder ☐

☐ + ☐ = ☐

☐ × ☐ = ☐

Sam needs to pay ☐ .

Worksheet 16

Solving Word Problems

Solve.

1 The teacher wants to pick one boy and one girl from the 10 children. How many different pairs could she choose?

$$\boxed{} \times \boxed{} = \boxed{}$$

There are $\boxed{}$ different pairs.

2 Ruby wants to buy a meal and a drink. How many different combinations can she choose?

Yum Lunch

Meal	Drinks
Hamburger	Soda
Pasta	Fruit Juice
Fish and Chips	Tea
Fried Chicken	
Pizza	

$$\boxed{} \times \boxed{} = \boxed{}$$

There are $\boxed{}$

different combinations.

Name: _____ Class: _____ Date: _____

Worksheet 17

Solving Word Problems

Solve.

1 Holly bought two packets of lollies.
The larger packet contained 12 more lollies than the smaller one.
The larger packet contained 32 lollies.
She divided the lollies equally into smaller goody bags.
Each goody bag had 7 lollies.

(a)   How many goody bags can Holly make?

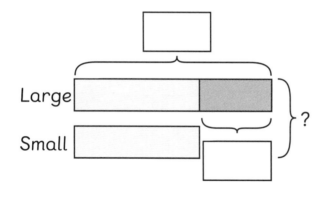

$$\boxed{} - \boxed{} = \boxed{}$$

$$\boxed{} + \boxed{} = \boxed{}$$

$$\boxed{} \div \boxed{} = \boxed{} \text{ remainder } \boxed{}$$

Holly can make $\boxed{}$ goody bags.

(b)   How many lollies were left over?

There were ⬚ lollies left over.

2 There are 8 more pupils in Class 4A than there are in Class 4B.
There are 28 pupils in Class 4A.
All the pupils must form teams.
Each team should have an equal number of pupils with nobody left out.
There should not be more than 10 pupils in each team.
What is the greatest number of teams they can form?

Worksheet 18

Solving Word Problems

Solve.

1 Sam has 5 times as many stickers as his brother has.
Together, both boys have 54 stickers.
How many stickers does Sam have?

Brother ☐

Sam ☐ ☐ ☐ ☐ ☐ } ☐

?

☐ ÷ ☐ = ☐

☐ × ☐ = ☐

Sam has ☐ stickers.

2 The mass of a rock is 7 times the mass of a brick.
The total mass of the rock and the brick together is 72 kg.
What is the mass of the rock?

3 A 56-m wire is cut into 3 parts.
The first part is twice as long as the second part and the second part is twice as long as the third part.
What is the length of the longest part?

Date: _____

Lulu bought some bars of chocolate to share equally with her friends.
She bought between 35 and 50 bars altogether.

If she shares the bars of chocolate equally with 7 friends,
she will have 7 bars left over.

If she shares the bar of chocolate equally with 6 friends,
she will have 5 bars left over.

How many bars of chocolate did she buy?

Review 3

1 Make a family of multiplication and division facts.

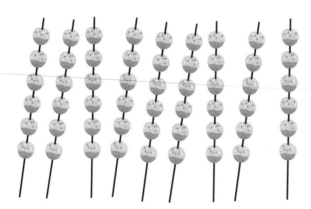

	×		=				÷		=	

	×		=				÷		=	

2 Complete the number patterns.

(a)   18, 24, 30, [   ] , 42, [   ]

(b)   35, [   ] , 49, [   ] , 63

(c)   16, [   ] , 32, 40, [   ]

(d)   [   ] , 54, 63, 72, [   ]

(e)   11, 22, [   ] , 44, [   ] ,66

(f)   12, 24, 36, 48, [   ] , [   ]

3 Match.

72 ÷ 9 ●	● 48 ●	● 0 × 1
1 × 24 ●	● 36 ●	● 4 × 12
6 × 6 ●	● 8 ●	● 63 ÷ 7
45 ÷ 5 ●	● 0 ●	● 4 × 9
12 × 0 ●	● 9 ●	● 64 ÷ 8
8 × 6 ●	● 24 ●	● 3 × 8

Solve.

4 Six 6-kg bags of rice are mixed with four 9-kg bags of rice.
Then the rice is repacked into 8-kg bags.
How many 8-kg bags will there be?

There will be ☐ 8-kg bags of rice.

5 Ruby has 4 different shirts and 3 different skirts.
She wants to wear a shirt with a skirt.
How many different ways can she create a matching outfit?

6 A building is 5 times as tall as a tree.
The total height of the building and the tree together is 48 m.
How tall is the building?

7 How much must you pay for 8 kg of ham and 9 kg of broccoli altogether?

£8 per kg

£3 per kg

Further Multiplication and Division

Chapter 4

Name: _____ Class: _____ Date: _____

Worksheet 1

Multiplying by 0 and 1

1 How many pineapples are there? Match.

 • • 5×1 • • 3

 • • 1×3 • • 0

 • • 2×4 • • 5

 • • 7×0 • • 8

 • • 3×2 • • 0

 • • 5×0 • • 6

2 Fill in the blanks.

(a) $1 \times 9 =$ ☐   (b) $9 \times 1 =$ ☐

(c) $1 \times 0 =$ ☐   (d) $0 \times 1 =$ ☐

(e) $0 \times 9 =$ ☐   (f) $9 \times 0 =$ ☐

(g) $8 \times 1 =$ ☐   (h) $8 \times 0 =$ ☐

(i) $1 \times 1 =$ ☐   (j) $1 \times 2 =$ ☐

3 Draw the correct number of cookies on each plate to show the multiplication fact.

(a)

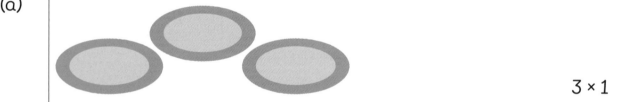

3×1

(b)

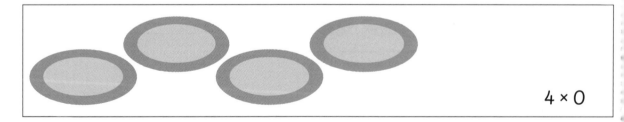

4×0

(c)

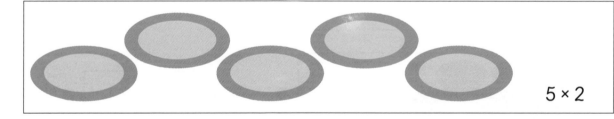

5×2

(d)

6×1

Name: _____ **Class:** _____ **Date:** _____

Worksheet 2

Dividing by 1

1 Circle the objects to make the number of groups required to show the division fact, and fill in each box.

(a)

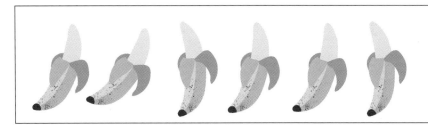

$6 \div 2 = \boxed{}$

(b)

$6 \div 3 = \boxed{}$

(c)

$6 \div 6 = \boxed{}$

(d)

$6 \div 1 = \boxed{}$

(e)

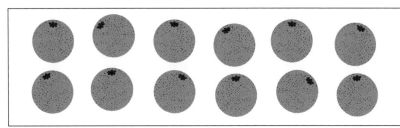

$12 \div 1 = \boxed{}$

2 Circle the calculations that equal 1.

4 ÷ 4

8 ÷ 4

4 ÷ 2   4 ÷ 1

8 ÷ 1

8 ÷ 8

6 ÷ 1

12 ÷ 12

6 ÷ 2

6 ÷ 6

3 Fill in the blanks.

(a)   10 ÷ 10 = ☐

10 ÷ 2 = ☐

10 ÷ 5 = ☐

10 ÷ 1 = ☐

(b)   9 ÷ 1 = ☐

9 ÷ 3 = ☐

9 ÷ 9 = ☐

(c)   7 ÷ 7 = ☐

5 ÷ 5 = ☐

3 ÷ 3 = ☐

1 ÷ 1 = ☐

(d)   7 ÷ 1 = ☐

5 ÷ 1 = ☐

3 ÷ 1 = ☐

12 ÷ 1 = ☐

Worksheet 3

Multiplying the Same Two Numbers

1 Draw circles to show the multiplication facts.
Fill in the blanks.

(a)

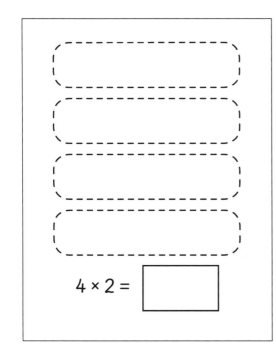

$4 \times 2 =$ ___

$2 \times 4 =$ ___

(b)

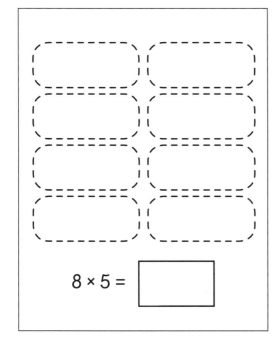

$8 \times 5 =$ ___

$5 \times 8 =$ ___

2 Fill in the blanks to complete Hannah's work.

$3 \times 4 = \boxed{4} + \boxed{4} + \boxed{4} = \boxed{}$

$4 \times 3 = \boxed{3} + \boxed{3} + \boxed{3} + \boxed{3} = \boxed{}$

$3 \times 4 = \boxed{} \times 3$

Use Hannah's method to fill in the blanks.

(a) $7 \times 5 = \boxed{} + \boxed{} + \boxed{} + \boxed{} + \boxed{} + \boxed{} + \boxed{} = \boxed{}$

$5 \times 7 = \boxed{} + \boxed{} + \boxed{} + \boxed{} + \boxed{} = \boxed{}$

$7 \times 5 = 5 \times \boxed{}$

(b) $15 \times 2 = \boxed{} \times 15$

$ = \boxed{} + \boxed{} = \boxed{}$

(c) $21 \times 3 = 3 \times \boxed{}$

$ = \boxed{} + \boxed{} + \boxed{} = \boxed{}$

(d) $25 \times 4 = \boxed{} \times 25$

$ = \boxed{} + \boxed{} + \boxed{} + \boxed{} = \boxed{}$

Worksheet 4

Multiplying Three Numbers

1 Draw circles to show the multiplication facts of three numbers.
Fill in the blanks.

(a)

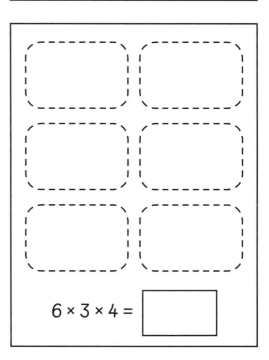

$5 × 2 × 3 =$ ☐

$5 × 2 × 3 =$ ☐

(b)

$6 × 3 × 4 =$ ☐

$6 × 3 × 4 =$ ☐

2 Sam learns two ways to multiply three numbers.

$5 \times 4 \times 3 = 5 \times$ [**12**]

$=$ [**12**] $+$ [**12**] $+$ [**12**] $+$ [**12**] $+$ [**12**]

$=$ [ ]

$5 \times 4 \times 3 =$ [**20**] $\times 3$

$=$ [**20**] $+$ [**20**] $+$ [**20**]

$=$ [ ]

Use Sam's method to find the products.

(a) $9 \times 2 \times 4 =$ [ ] $\times 4$

$=$ [ ] $+$ [ ] $+$ [ ] $+$ [ ]

$=$ [ ]

| (   ) | (   ) | (   ) | (   ) |

(   )

(b) $3 \times 6 \times 5 =$ [ ]

(c) $5 \times 7 \times 4 =$ [ ]

Worksheet 5

Multiplying Multiples of 10

1 Amira found the value of 5 × 30 using three different methods.
Fill in the missing numbers.

5 × 30 = | 30 | + | 30 | + | 30 | + | 30 | + | 30 | = | ☐ |

5 × 30 = 5 × | 3 | tens = | 15 | tens = | ☐ |

5 × 30 = 5 × 3 × | 10 | = | 15 | × | 10 | = | ☐ |

Use Amira's methods to find the products.

(a) 8 × 50 = ☐ + ☐ + ☐ + ☐

+ ☐ + ☐ + ☐ + ☐ = ☐

8 × 50 = 8 × ☐ tens = ☐ tens = ☐

8 × 50 = 8 × 5 × ☐ = ☐ × ☐ = ☐

(b) 90 × 4 = ☐ + ☐ + ☐ + ☐ = ☐

90 × 4 = 4 × ☐ tens = ☐ tens = ☐

90 × 4 = 4 × 9 × ☐ = ☐ × ☐ = ☐

2 Match.

70 × 6 ●	● 560
9 × 30 ●	● 100
5 × 50 ●	● 420
8 × 70 ●	● 270
20 × 5 ●	● 250

3 Multiply.

(a) 6 × 40 = ☐

(b) 7 × 90 = ☐

(c) 8 × 60 = ☐

(d) 9 × 50 = ☐

(e) 11 × 20 = ☐

(f) 10 × 30 = ☐

(g) 70 × 4 = ☐

(h) 80 × 8 = ☐

(i) 90 × 8 = ☐

(j) 30 × 6 = ☐

(k) 7 × 70 = ☐

(l) 5 × 50 = ☐

Name: _____ Class: _____ Date: _____

Multiplying 2-Digit Numbers

1 Multiply.

(a)　12 × 3 = ☐

$$\begin{array}{r} 1\ \ 2 \\ \times\ \ \ \ 3 \\ \hline \end{array}$$

+ _____
_____

(b)　54 × 2 = ☐

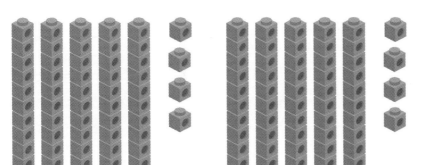

$$\begin{array}{r} 5\ \ 4 \\ \times\ \ \ \ 2 \\ \hline \end{array}$$

+ _____
_____

(c)　22 × 4 = ☐

20	2
20	2
20	2
20	2

$$\begin{array}{r} 2\ \ 2 \\ \times\ \ \ \ 4 \\ \hline \end{array}$$

+ _____
_____

2 Sam and Amira found the product of 41 and 2 in two different ways.

| 40 | × 2 = | 80 |

| 1 | × 2 = | 2 |

| 80 | + | 2 | = | |

41 × 2 =

41

(40) (1)

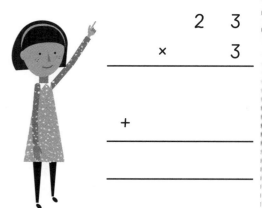

```
      4  1
   ×     2
   _____
         2
+     8  0
   _____
      8  2
```

Use their methods to find the product of 23 and 3.

Sam's method

| | × 3 = | |

| | × 3 = | |

| | + | | = | |

23 × 3 =

23

(20) ( )

Amira's method

```
      2  3
   ×     3
   _____
+
   _____
   _____
```

3 Multiply.

(a) 31 × 3 =

(b) 4 × 21 =

(c) 34 × 2 =

(d) 2 × 22 =

(e) 14 × 2 =

(f) 32 × 2 =

(g) 3 × 33 =

(h) 2 × 43 =

(i) 51 × 2 =

(j) 42 × 2 =

Worksheet 7

Multiplying 2-Digit Numbers

1 Multiply.

(a) $37 \times 4 =$ [   ]

$7 \times 4 =$ [   ]

$30 \times 4 =$ [   ]

[   ] + [   ] = [   ]

$$\begin{array}{r} 3\ \ 7 \\ \times \quad\ 4 \\ \hline \\ + \\ \hline \\ \hline \end{array}$$

(b) $56 \times 7 =$ [   ]

$6 \times 7 =$ [   ]

$50 \times 7 =$ [   ]

[   ] + [   ] = [   ]

$$\begin{array}{r} 5\ \ 6 \\ \times \quad\ 7 \\ \hline \\ + \\ \hline \\ \hline \end{array}$$

(c) $38 \times 8 =$ [   ]

$8 \times 8 =$ [   ]

$30 \times 8 =$ [   ]

[   ] + [   ] = [   ]

$$\begin{array}{r} 3\ \ 8 \\ \times \quad\ 8 \\ \hline \\ + \\ \hline \\ \hline \end{array}$$

2 Fill in the blanks.

(a) $26 \times 9 = \boxed{}$

$\boxed{} \times 9 = \boxed{}$

$\boxed{} \times 9 = \boxed{}$

$\boxed{} + \boxed{} = \boxed{}$

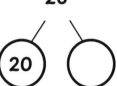

26

20 ◯

$$\begin{array}{r} 2\ \ 6 \\ \times \quad 9 \\ \hline \\ + \\ \hline \\ \hline \end{array}$$

(b) $64 \times 5 = \boxed{}$

$\boxed{} \times 5 = \boxed{}$

$\boxed{} \times 5 = \boxed{}$

$\boxed{} + \boxed{} = \boxed{}$

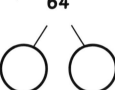

64

◯ ◯

$$\begin{array}{r} 6\ \ 4 \\ \times \quad 5 \\ \hline \\ + \\ \hline \\ \hline \end{array}$$

3 Multiply.

(a) $18 \times 2 = \boxed{}$

(b) $3 \times 25 = \boxed{}$

(c) $4 \times 29 = \boxed{}$

(d) $32 \times 6 = \boxed{}$

(e) $43 \times 5 = \boxed{}$

(f) $56 \times 4 = \boxed{}$

(g) $7 \times 53 = \boxed{}$

(h) $8 \times 66 = \boxed{}$

(i) $23 \times 9 = \boxed{}$

(j) $89 \times 8 = \boxed{}$

Name: _____ Class: _____ Date: _____

Multiplying Multiples of 100

1 Amira found the value of 4 × 200 in three ways.
Fill in the missing numbers.

4 × 200 = | **200** | + | **200** | + | **200** | + | **200** | = | ☐ |

4 × 200 = 4 × | **2** | hundreds = | **8** | hundreds = | ☐ |

4 × 200 = 4 × 2 × | **100** | = | **8** | × | **100** | = | ☐ |

Use Amira's methods to find the products.

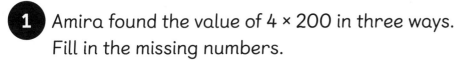

(a) 9 × 600 = ☐ + ☐ + ☐ + ☐ + ☐

☐ + ☐ + ☐ + ☐ = ☐

9 × 600 = 9 × ☐ hundreds = ☐ hundreds = ☐

9 × 600 = 9 × 6 × ☐ = ☐ × ☐ = ☐

(b) 500 × 5 = ☐ + ☐ + ☐ + ☐ + ☐

= ☐

500 × 5 = 5 × ☐ hundreds = ☐ hundreds = ☐

500 × 5 = 5 × 5 × ☐ = ☐ × ☐ = ☐

2 Circle the two numbers that give the product shown on the left.

1200	2	3	4	100	200	300

1500	3	4	5	400	500	600

900	1	2	3	200	300	400

3600	6	7	8	400	500	600

2800	7	8	9	300	400	500

4800	5	6	7	600	700	800

3 Multiply.

(a) $3 \times 600 =$

(b) $4 \times 800 =$

(c) $6 \times 900 =$

(d) $6 \times 300 =$

(e) $9 \times 500 =$

(f) $10 \times 700 =$

(g) $800 \times 7 =$

(h) $500 \times 6 =$

(i) $9 \times 700 =$

(j) $11 \times 400 =$

Worksheet 9

Multiplying 3-Digit Numbers

1 Multiply to find:

(a) $431 \times 2 =$ ▢

  $400 \times 2 =$ ▢

  $30 \times 2 =$ ▢

  $1 \times 2 =$ ▢

  ▢ + ▢ + ▢

  = ▢

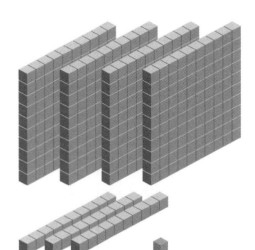

(b) $323 \times 3 =$ ▢

  $300 \times 3 =$ ▢

  $20 \times 3 =$ ▢

  $3 \times 3 =$ ▢

  ▢ + ▢ + ▢

  = ▢

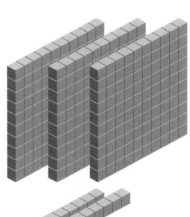

2 Fill in the blanks to calculate:

(a) $403 \times 2 = \boxed{}$

$$\boxed{} \times 2 = \boxed{}$$

$$\boxed{} \times 2 = \boxed{}$$

$$\boxed{} + \boxed{} = \boxed{}$$

403

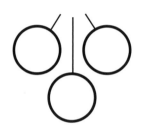

```
        4   0   3
    ×           2
  _____

  +
  _____

  _____
```

(b) $312 \times 3 = \boxed{}$

$$\boxed{} \times 3 = \boxed{}$$

$$\boxed{} \times 3 = \boxed{}$$

$$\boxed{} \times 3 = \boxed{}$$

$$\boxed{} + \boxed{} + \boxed{} = \boxed{}$$

312

```
        3   1   2
    ×           3
  _____

  +
  _____

  _____
```

3 Multiply.

(a) $102 \times 3 = \boxed{}$

(b) $3 \times 321 = \boxed{}$

(c) $4 \times 211 = \boxed{}$

(d) $342 \times 2 = \boxed{}$

(e) $333 \times 3 = \boxed{}$

(f) $144 \times 2 = \boxed{}$

(g) $2 \times 443 = \boxed{}$

(h) $3 \times 203 = \boxed{}$

(i) $220 \times 4 = \boxed{}$

(j) $504 \times 2 = \boxed{}$

Worksheet 10

Multiplying 3-Digit Numbers

1 Multiply to find:

(a) $123 \times 4 =$ [ ]

$100 \times 4 =$ [ ]

$20 \times 4 =$ [ ]

$3 \times 4 =$ [ ]

[ ] + [ ] + [ ]

= [ ]

(b) $217 \times 3 =$ [ ]

$200 \times 3 =$ [ ]

$10 \times 3 =$ [ ]

$7 \times 3 =$ [ ]

[ ] + [ ] + [ ]

= [ ]

(c) $719 \times 5 =$ [ ]

$700 \times 5 =$ [ ]

$10 \times 5 =$ [ ]

$9 \times 5 =$ [ ]

[ ] + [ ] + [ ]

= [ ]

(d) $806 \times 7 =$ [ ]

$800 \times 7 =$ [ ]

$0 \times 7 =$ [ ]

$6 \times 7 =$ [ ]

[ ] + [ ] + [ ]

= [ ]

2 Multiply.

(a)
```
    3  1  6
  ×       6
  _____


  +
  _____

  _____
```
316 × 6 = ☐

(b)
```
    4  2  3
  ×       4
  _____


  +
  _____

  _____
```
423 × 4 = ☐

(c)
```
    9  1  3
  ×       7
  _____


  +
  _____

  _____
```
913 × 7 = ☐

(d)
```
    5  1  6
  ×       5
  _____


  +
  _____

  _____
```
516 × 5 = ☐

3 Multiply.

(a) 118 × 3 = ☐

(b) 4 × 218 = ☐

(c) 5 × 215 = ☐

(d) 349 × 2 = ☐

(e) 324 × 3 = ☐

(f) 637 × 2 = ☐

(g) 2 × 435 = ☐

(h) 3 × 629 = ☐

(i) 719 × 5 = ☐

(j) 524 × 4 = ☐

Worksheet 11

Multiplying 3-Digit Numbers

1 Multiply to find:

(a) $271 \times 8 = \boxed{}$

$200 \times 8 = \boxed{}$

$70 \times 8 = \boxed{}$

$1 \times 8 = \boxed{}$

$\boxed{} + \boxed{} + \boxed{}$

$= \boxed{}$

(b) $345 \times 6 = \boxed{}$

$300 \times 6 = \boxed{}$

$40 \times 6 = \boxed{}$

$5 \times 6 = \boxed{}$

$\boxed{} + \boxed{} + \boxed{}$

$= \boxed{}$

(c) $577 \times 5 = \boxed{}$

$500 \times 5 = \boxed{}$

$70 \times 5 = \boxed{}$

$7 \times 5 = \boxed{}$

$\boxed{} + \boxed{} + \boxed{}$

$= \boxed{}$

(d) $678 \times 9 = \boxed{}$

$600 \times 9 = \boxed{}$

$70 \times 9 = \boxed{}$

$8 \times 9 = \boxed{}$

$\boxed{} + \boxed{} + \boxed{}$

$= \boxed{}$

2 Multiply.

(a)
```
    7  4  7
  ×        7
  ─────────

  +
  ─────────

  ─────────
```
747 × 7 = ☐

(b)
```
    5  6  4
  ×        3
  ─────────

  +
  ─────────

  ─────────
```
564 × 3 = ☐

(c)
```
    8  5  2
  ×        4
  ─────────

  +
  ─────────

  ─────────
```
852 × 4 = ☐

(d)
```
    4  8  8
  ×        8
  ─────────

  +
  ─────────

  ─────────
```
488 × 8 = ☐

3 Multiply.

(a) 186 × 3 = ☐

(b) 4 × 627 = ☐

(c) 7 × 366 = ☐

(d) 6 × 465 = ☐

(e) 633 × 5 = ☐

(f) 953 × 2 = ☐

(g) 8 × 379 = ☐

(h) 9 × 297 = ☐

(i) 687 × 9 = ☐

(j) 532 × 7 = ☐

Worksheet 12

Dividing 2-Digit Numbers

1 Circle the discs to show the division facts.
Fill in the blanks.

(a) 39 ÷ 3

= [ ]

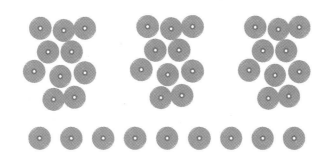

(b) 88 ÷ 4

= [ ]

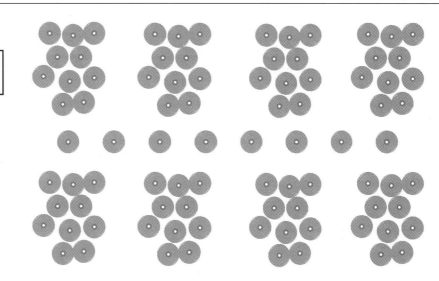

(c) 64 ÷ 2

= [ ]

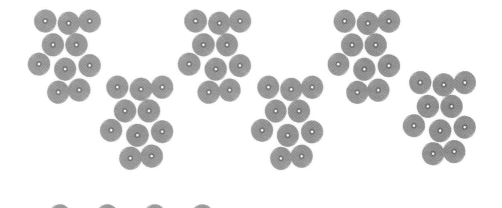

2 Divide to find:

(a) $77 \div 7 =$ ☐

$70 \div 7 =$ ☐

$7 \div 7 =$ ☐

☐ $+$ ☐ $=$ ☐

(b) $96 \div 3 =$ ☐

$90 \div 3 =$ ☐

$6 \div 3 =$ ☐

☐ $+$ ☐ $=$ ☐

(c) $36 \div 2 =$ ☐

$30 \div 2 =$ ☐

$6 \div 2 =$ ☐

☐ $+$ ☐ $=$ ☐

(d) $55 \div 5 =$ ☐

$50 \div 5 =$ ☐

$5 \div 5 =$ ☐

☐ $+$ ☐ $=$ ☐

3 Divide.

(a) $42 \div 2 =$ ☐

(b) $36 \div 3 =$ ☐

(c) $62 \div 2 =$ ☐

(d) $66 \div 6 =$ ☐

(e) $84 \div 4 =$ ☐

(f) $66 \div 3 =$ ☐

(g) $88 \div 8 =$ ☐

(h) $66 \div 2 =$ ☐

Name: _____ Class: _____ Date: _____

Worksheet 13

Dividing 3-Digit Numbers

1 Circle the discs to show the division facts.
Fill in the blanks.

(a) 246 ÷ 2

= [ ]

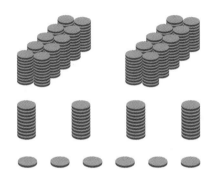

(b) 639 ÷ 3

= [ ]

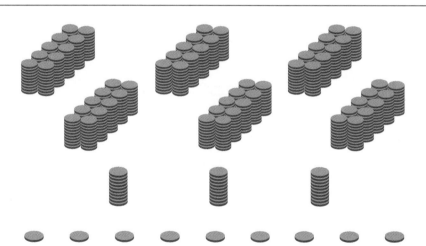

(c) 804 ÷ 4

= [ ]

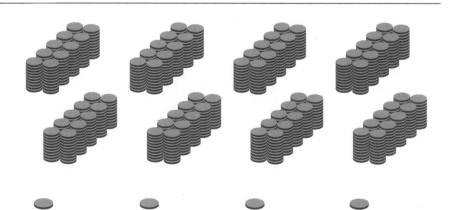

2 Divide to find:

(a) $888 \div 8 = \boxed{}$

$800 \div 8 = \boxed{}$

$80 \div 8 = \boxed{}$

$8 \div 8 = \boxed{}$

$\boxed{} + \boxed{} + \boxed{} = \boxed{}$

(b) $696 \div 3 = \boxed{}$

$600 \div 3 = \boxed{}$

$90 \div 3 = \boxed{}$

$6 \div 3 = \boxed{}$

$\boxed{} + \boxed{} + \boxed{} = \boxed{}$

(c) $824 \div 2 = \boxed{}$

$800 \div 2 = \boxed{}$

$20 \div 2 = \boxed{}$

$4 \div 2 = \boxed{}$

$\boxed{} + \boxed{} + \boxed{} = \boxed{}$

(d) $550 \div 5 = \boxed{}$

$500 \div 5 = \boxed{}$

$50 \div 5 = \boxed{}$

$\boxed{} + \boxed{} = \boxed{}$

3 Divide.

(a) $248 \div 2 = \boxed{}$

(b) $806 \div 2 = \boxed{}$

(c) $369 \div 3 = \boxed{}$

(d) $555 \div 5 = \boxed{}$

(e) $848 \div 4 = \boxed{}$

(f) $707 \div 7 = \boxed{}$

(g) $999 \div 9 = \boxed{}$

(h) $880 \div 4 = \boxed{}$

(i) $660 \div 6 = \boxed{}$

(j) $486 \div 2 = \boxed{}$

Worksheet 14

Dividing 2-Digit Numbers

1 Divide.

(a) $90 \div 6$

$=$ [ ]

$6\overline{)9\ 0}$

(b) $97 \div 3$

$=$ [ ]

$3\overline{)9\ 7}$

(c) $79 \div 4$

$=$ [ ]

$4\overline{)7\ 9}$

(d) $88 \div 5$

$=$ [ ]

$5\overline{)8\ 8}$

(e) $96 \div 8$

$=$ [ ]

$8\overline{)9\ 6}$

(f) $99 \div 9$

$=$ [ ]

$9\overline{)9\ 9}$

Worksheet 15

Dividing 3-Digit Numbers

1 Divide.

(a) $118 \div 2$

= ⬚

$2 \overline{)118}$

(b) $120 \div 8$

= ⬚

$8 \overline{)120}$

(c) $420 \div 4$

= ⬚

$4 \overline{)420}$

(d) $288 \div 9$

= ⬚

$9 \overline{)288}$

(e) $336 \div 6$

= ⬚

$6 \overline{)336}$

(f) $735 \div 7$

= ⬚

$7 \overline{)735}$

Worksheet 16

Dividing 3-Digit Numbers

1 Divide.

(a) $163 \div 3$

= [   ] $3\overline{)163}$

(b) $254 \div 4$

= [   ] $4\overline{)254}$

(c) $357 \div 6$

= [   ] $6\overline{)357}$

(d) $436 \div 8$

= [   ] $8\overline{)436}$

(e) $590 \div 7$

= [   ] $7\overline{)590}$

(f) $825 \div 9$

= [   ] $9\overline{)825}$

2 There are 500 pupils.

They are asked to form groups of a fixed size.

What is the largest number of groups they can form?

(a) What if there are 6 pupils in each group?

$500 \div 6 = \boxed{}$

$6 \overline{)500}$

The largest number of groups they can

form is $\boxed{}$.

(b) What if there are 7 pupils in each group?

$500 \div 7 = \boxed{}$

$7 \overline{)500}$

The largest number of groups they can

form is $\boxed{}$.

(c) What if there are 8 pupils in each group?

$500 \div 8 = \boxed{}$

$8 \overline{)500}$

The largest number of groups they can

form is $\boxed{}$.

(d) What if there are 9 pupils in each group?

$500 \div 9 = \boxed{}$

$9 \overline{)500}$

The largest number of groups they can

form is $\boxed{}$.

Name: _____ Class: _____ Date: _____

Worksheet 17

Solving Word Problems

Solve.

1 There are 156 sheep on a farm.
The farm has 3 times as many cows as sheep.
(a)   How many cows are on the farm?

(b)   What is the combined number of sheep and cows on the farm?

3 The library has 441 storybooks and magazines altogether.
There are 8 times as many storybooks as magazines.
How many more storybooks than magazines are there in the library?

4 Charles has 9 times as many red marbles as blue marbles.
If he has 288 more red than blue marbles, how many red marbles does he have?

A bakery sells cupcakes in small boxes of 2 or regular boxes of 6.

The bakery baked 188 cupcakes.

After packing them into the boxes, there were 2 more regular boxes than there were small boxes.

How many small boxes and regular boxes of cupcakes were there altogether?

Review 4

1 Fill in the blanks.

(a) $7 \times 6 = \boxed{} + \boxed{} + \boxed{} + \boxed{} + \boxed{} + \boxed{} + \boxed{}$

$= \boxed{}$

$6 \times 7 = \boxed{} + \boxed{} + \boxed{} + \boxed{} + \boxed{} + \boxed{} = \boxed{}$

$7 \times 6 = 6 \times \boxed{}$

(b) $7 \times 8 \times 3 = \boxed{} \times 3$

$= \boxed{} + \boxed{} + \boxed{} = \boxed{}$

2 Match.

500×6	6×0	5×60	1×5	$900 \div 9$	$600 \div 6$
●	●	●	●	●	●

●	●	●	●	●	●
0	3000	5	100	300	100

3 Multiply.

(a)
```
      5  7
  ×      6
_____

+
_____

_____
```

(b)
```
      6  9
  ×      8
_____

+
_____

_____
```

(c)
```
   8  4  2
  ×      7
_____

+
_____

_____
```

(d)
```
   2  3  9
  ×      9
_____

+
_____

_____
```

4 Divide.

(a) $95 \div 3$

= [   ] $3\overline{)9\ 5}$

(b) $97 \div 4$

= [   ] $4\overline{)9\ 7}$

(c) $725 \div 7$

= [   ] $7\overline{)7\ 2\ 5}$

(d) $867 \div 9$

= [   ] $9\overline{)8\ 6\ 7}$

Solve.

5 The aquarium has 198 guppies, angelfish and catfish altogether.
There are 4 times as many guppies as angelfish. There are 6 more
angelfish than catfish.
How many catfish are there?

6 A bag of 8 sausages costs £9.
Sam has £120.
At the very most, how many sausages can Sam buy?

Name: _____ Class: _____ Date: _____

Revision 1

1 Count and then write the numbers in numerals and in words.

	Numeral	Words
1000 1000		
100 100 100 100		
10 10 10		
1000 1000 100 100 100 100 100 10 1		

2 Arrange the numbers from greatest to smallest.

(a)   1250, 5021, 1205, 5102

(b)   8433, 8334, 8443, 8343

3 Find the missing numbers.

(a)   9889 is ⬚ more than 9789.

(b)   5236 is ⬚ less than 6236.

(c)   4724 is 1000 more than ⬚.

(d)   7999 is 100 less than ⬚.

4 Fill in the blanks.

can of soda
330 ml

mineral water
1550 ml

mug of hot chocolate
735 ml

(a)   The total volume of a can of soda and a mug of hot chocolate is ⬚ ml.

(b)   The difference in volume between a bottle of mineral water and a mug of hot chocolate is ⬚ ml.

(c)   The total volume of 9 cans of soda is ⬚ ml.

5 Solve.

Show your work clearly.

(a)
```
    8   6   0   4
-   4   6   5   6
─────────────────


─────────────────
```

(b)
```
    4   9   6   5
-   4   8   7   9
─────────────────


─────────────────
```

(c)
```
        7   5
×           8
─────────────
```

(d)
```
        3   6   9
×               7
─────────────────
```

(e) 9) 6   0   3

(f) 6) 5   1   7

6 Ravi had 237 marbles more than Elliott had.
Ravi gave Elliott 165 marbles.
Who had more marbles in the end?
How many more?

7 There are 2918 male workers in a factory.
There are 1264 fewer male than female workers.
How many male and female workers are there in the factory altogether?

8 A bag of flour is 6 times as heavy as a packet of sugar.
The total mass of the flour and sugar is 3612 g.
What is the mass of the bag of flour?

9 A box of 9 doughnuts costs £6.
Holly has £100.
At the very most, how many doughnuts can she
buy with her money?

10 The coffee shop sells 5 different types of cake and 6 different kinds of drinks.

Ruby wants to order a cake and a drink.

How many different combinations of cake and drink could she choose?

Graphs

Chapter 5

Name: _____ Class: _____ Date: _____

Worksheet 1

Drawing and Reading Picture Graphs and Bar Graphs

1 The table below shows the number of burgers sold in a café from Monday to Friday.

Monday	Tuesday	Wednesday	Thursday	Friday
62	80	73	82	94

Sam drew a bar graph to show the number of burgers sold.
Complete Sam's graph.

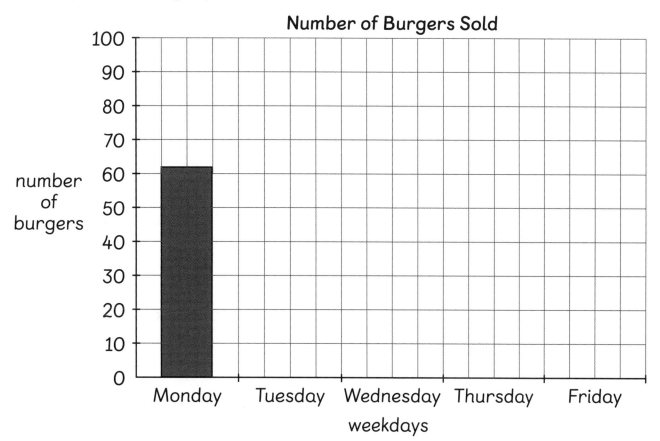

2 This bar graph shows the number of chicken pies sold in the same café from Monday to Friday.

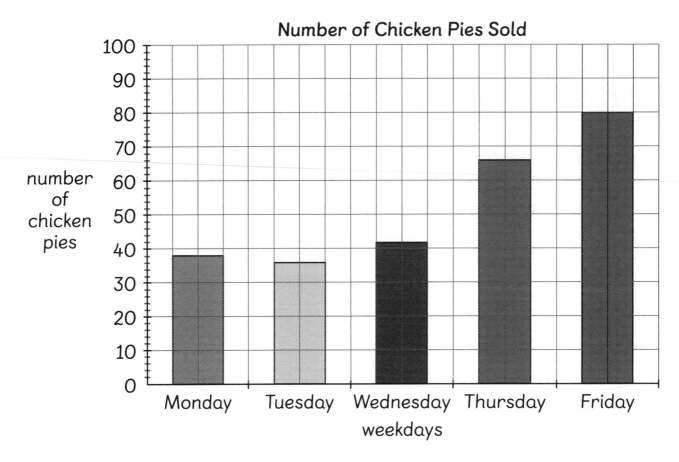

(a) ☐ chicken pies were sold on Monday and Tuesday altogether.

(b) The most chicken pies were sold on ☐ and the least number

of chicken pies were sold on ☐ .

(c) ☐ more chicken pies were sold on Thursday than on

Wednesday.

(d) Which was a more popular choice in the café, the burgers

(Question 1) or the chicken pies? Explain your answer.

☐

Name: _____ Class: _____ Date: _____

Worksheet 2

Drawing and Reading Bar Graphs

This table shows four children's scores in a game.

Name	Sam	Hannah	Emma	Elliott
Score	64	23	38	48

1 Draw a bar graph to show the scores.

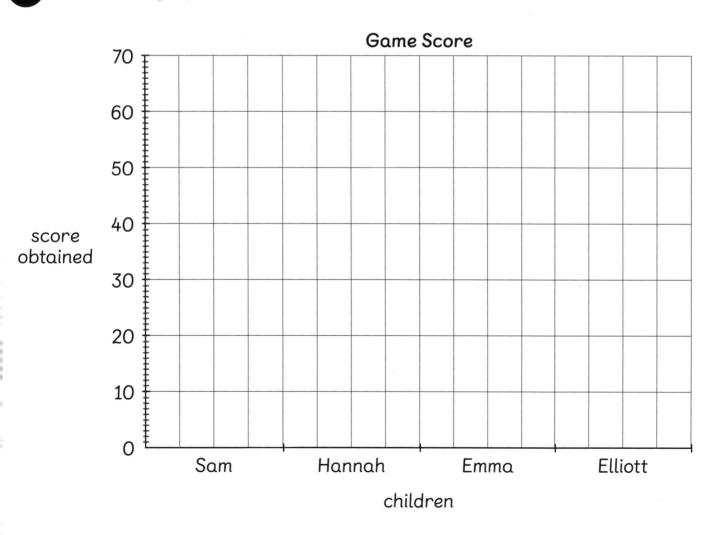

2 Look at the bar graph and fill in the boxes.

(a) [ ] has the highest score.

(b) [ ] has the lowest score.

(c) Elliott's score is [ ] points higher than Hannah's.

(d) Hannah's score is [ ] points lower than Emma's.

(e) The difference between the highest and lowest score is [ ] .

(f) Elliott wants to score 80 points in the next game. How many more points does he need in order to reach his goal?

He needs [ ] more points.

(g) Complete this table to show the total scores.

Who has the higher total: the boys or the girls?

	Boys	Girls
Score		

The [ ] have the higher total.

Worksheet 3

Drawing and Reading Line Graphs

1 The table below shows the change in the price of Brand A chocolates over the years.

Year	2005	2007	2009	2011	2013	2015
Price	£2.50	£2.00	£2.50	£3.00	£3.50	£4.00

Draw a line graph to show the information in the table.

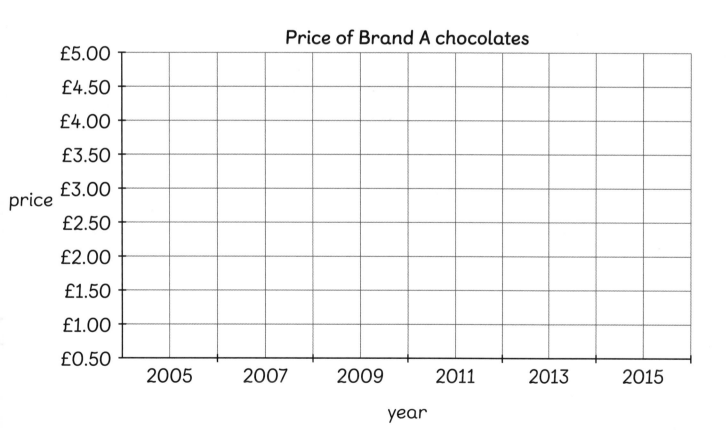

(a)   What was the price of Brand A chocolates in 2005?

(b)   What was the price of Brand A chocolates in 2011?

(c)   What is the difference in price between 2005
        and 2015?

(d)   In which year was the price of Brand A chocolates
        the lowest?

(e)   Between which two years was the price difference
        the greatest?

(f)   In which year did the price of Brand A chocolates
        drop?

(g)   Circle the correct answer.
        The price of Brand A chocolates (increased / decreased)
        from 2005 to 2007 but (increased / decreased)
        from 2007 to 2015.

2 The line graph below shows the number of patients at a dental clinic from 9 a.m. to 12 noon.

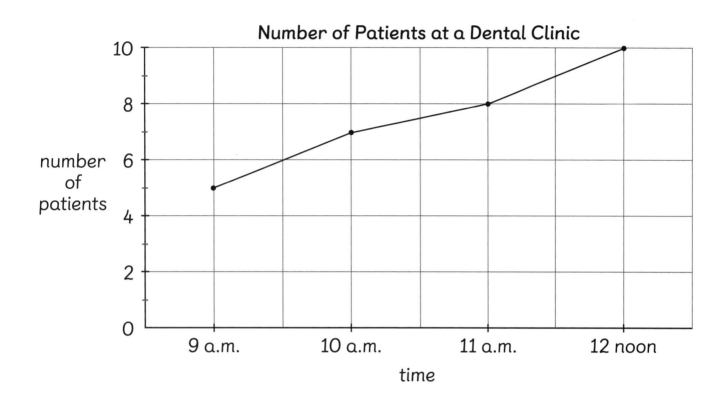

(a) At what time was there the most patients?

(b) At what time was there the least number of patients?

(c) What was the difference between the number of patients at 10 a.m. and at 12 noon?

(d) Did the number of patients increase or decrease from 9 a.m. to 12 noon?

Worksheet 4

Drawing and Reading Line Graphs

A beaker of water was left on the table to evaporate for 5 hours. The amount of water in the beaker was recorded every hour.

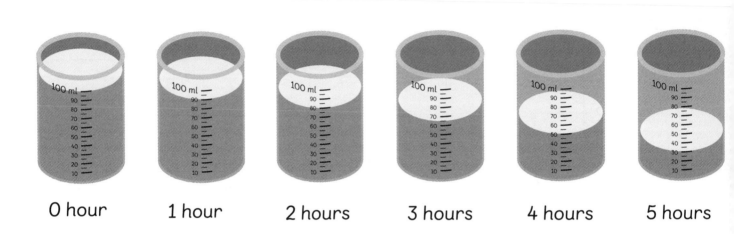

| 0 hour | 1 hour | 2 hours | 3 hours | 4 hours | 5 hours |

1 Complete the table to show the amount of water in the beaker after every hour.

Time (h)	0	1	2	3	4	5
Amount of water (ml)						

2 Draw a line graph to show the amount of water in the beaker over the 5-hour period.

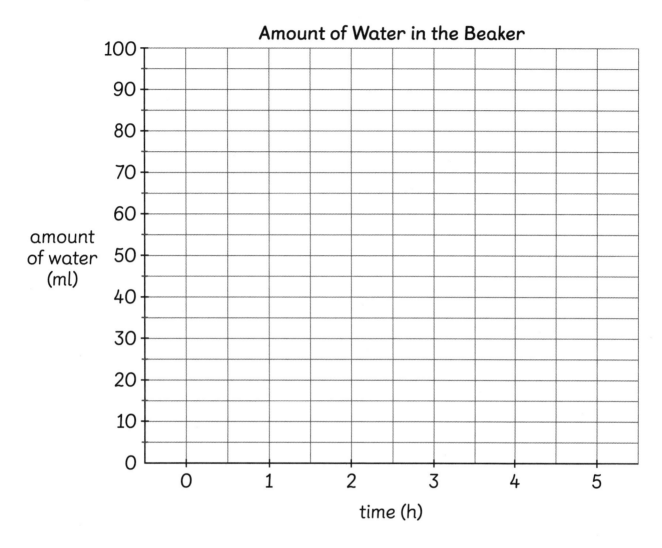

Amount of Water in the Beaker

amount of water (ml)

time (h)

(a) How much water was in the beaker at first?

(b) How much water was lost after 5 hours?

(c) After how many hours did the beaker lose half the original amount of water?

3 Another beaker of water was left to evaporate for 5 hours. The amount of water in the beaker was also recorded hourly.

A line graph showing the amount of water in the beaker over the 5-hour period is drawn below.

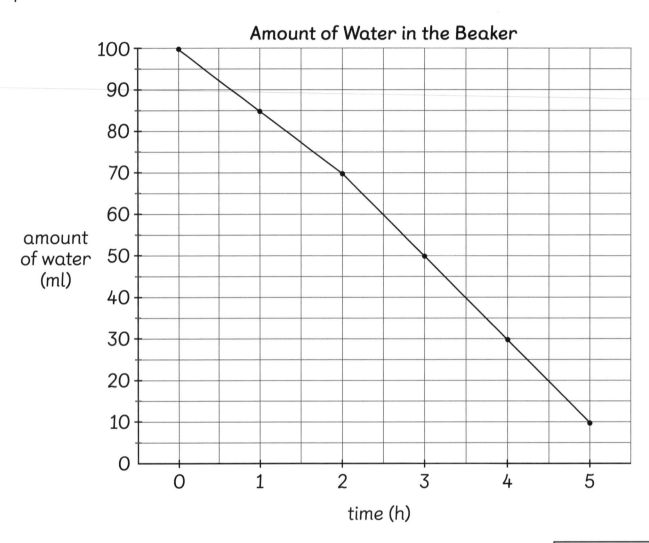

(a)   How much water was left in the beaker after 5 hours?

(b)   How much water was lost after 5 hours?

(c)   Compare the water loss from this beaker with that from the beaker in Question 2.
Which beaker lost more water over 5 hours?

Worksheet 5

Drawing and Reading Line Graphs

The line graph below shows the number of cars sold by Company A from May to October in a particular year.

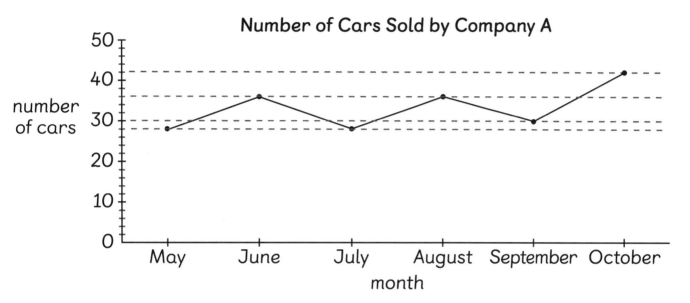

The line graph below shows the number of cars sold by Company B from May to October in the same year.

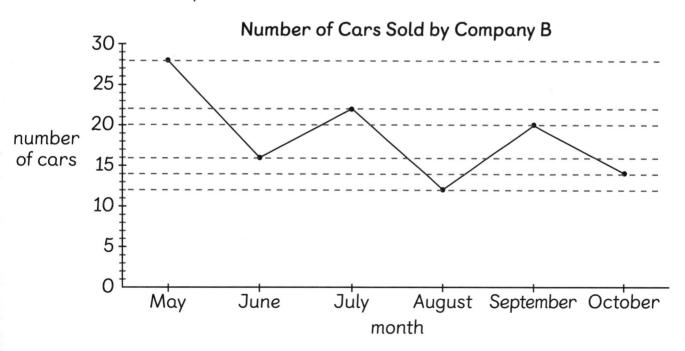

1 Complete the table below to compare the number of cars sold by Company A and Company B from May to October.

Month	Company A	Company B
May		
June		
July		
August		
September		
October		

2 Circle the correct answers.

(a) There was (an increase / a decrease) in the number of cars sold by Company A from May to October.

(b) There was (an increase / a decrease) in the number of cars sold by Company B from May to October.

(c) (More / Fewer) cars were sold by Company A than by Company B from May to October.

3 Draw two line graphs on the same grid to show the number of cars sold by Company A and Company B from May to October.

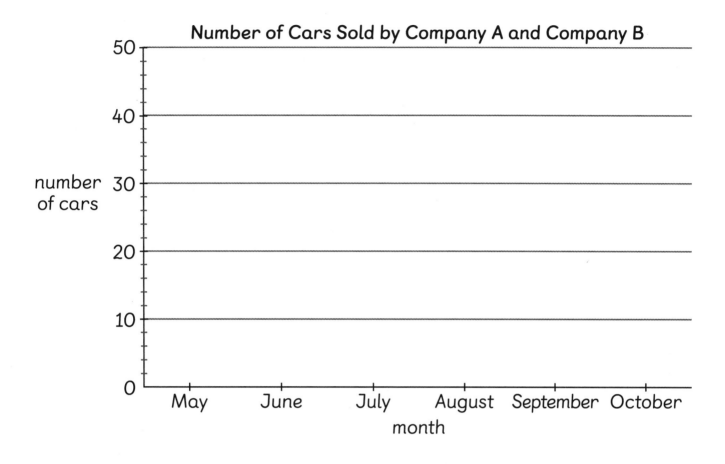

(a) What was the difference between the numbers of cars sold by Company A and by Company B in June?

(b) In which month was the difference the greatest? What was this difference?

Date: _____

1 Here are some patterns formed using matchsticks.
Complete the table.

Figure 1   Figure 2   Figure 3   Figure 4

Complete the table below.

Figure	1	2	3	4
Number of triangles	1			
Number of matchsticks	3			

2 Draw a line graph to show how the number of matchsticks used changes with the number of triangles formed.

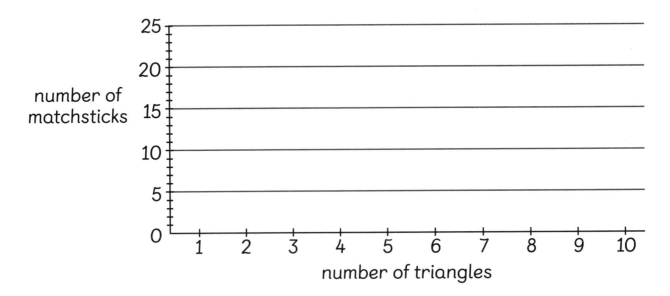

3 How many matchsticks are needed to form the pattern with 10 triangles? Does your answer agree with the graph in Question 2?

Name: _____ Class: _____ Date: _____

Review 5

1 The bar graph below shows the number of storybooks that Ruby read each week during the month of January.

The Number of Storybooks Read

Week 4

Week 3

Week 2

Week 1

0   5   10   15   20   25   30

storybooks

(a) How many storybooks did Ruby read in Week 3?

(b) In which week did Ruby read the least number of storybooks?

(c) How many books did Ruby read altogether in the month of January?

(d) In which two weeks was the difference in the number of books read the greatest?
What was this difference?

2 The line graph below shows the number of diners visiting a restaurant each day from Wednesday to Sunday.

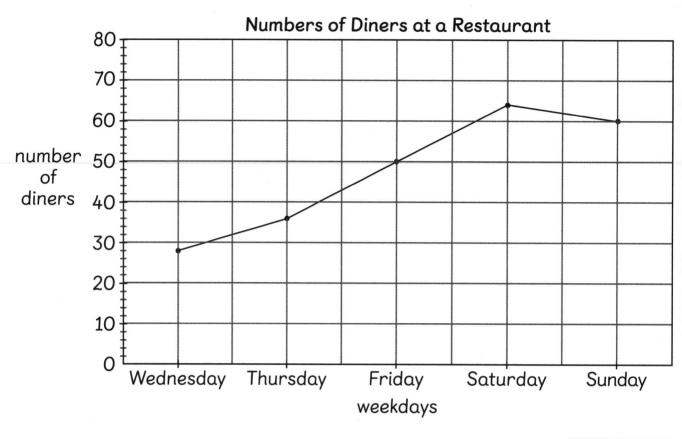

(a) How many diners were there on Friday?

(b) On which day was there the greatest number of diners?

(c) How many diners were there at the restaurant altogether from Wednesday to Sunday?

(d) What was the difference between the number of diners on Wednesday and on Saturday?

(e) Did the number of diners increase or decrease from Saturday to Sunday?

Fractions

Name: _____ Class: _____ Date: _____

Worksheet 1

Counting in Hundredths

1 What fraction of the block is shaded?

(a)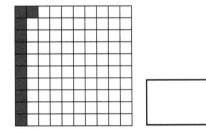

(b)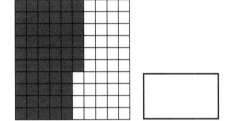

2 Fill in the blanks.

(a)

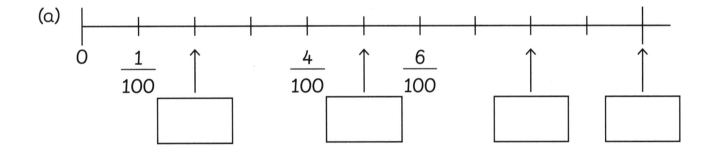

$\dfrac{1}{100}$ $\dfrac{4}{100}$ $\dfrac{6}{100}$

(b) ☐ , $\dfrac{19}{100}$, $\dfrac{20}{100}$, $\dfrac{21}{100}$, ☐ , $\dfrac{23}{100}$, $\dfrac{24}{100}$, ☐

(c) $\dfrac{89}{100}$, ☐ , $\dfrac{85}{100}$, $\dfrac{83}{100}$, ☐ , $\dfrac{79}{100}$, ☐ , $\dfrac{75}{100}$

Worksheet 2

Writing Mixed Numbers

1 What is the total number of pizzas?

□ + □ = □

There are □ pizzas altogether.

2 How many beakers of water are there?

□ + □ = □

There are □ beakers of water.

3 How many bars of chocolate are there?

□ + □ = □

There are □ bars of chocolate.

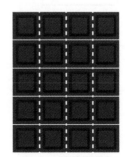

4 What are the mixed numbers shown?

(a)

$3 + \dfrac{1}{3} =$ ⬚   3 and 1 third is ⬚.

(b)

$2 + \dfrac{3}{5} =$ ⬚   2 and 3 fifths is ⬚.

(c)

$4 + \dfrac{1}{4} =$ ⬚   4 and 1 quarter is ⬚.

(d)

$1 + \dfrac{5}{6} =$ ⬚   1 and 5 sixths is ⬚.

(e)

$2 + \dfrac{3}{7} =$ ⬚   2 and 3 sevenths is ⬚.

Worksheet 3

Showing Mixed Numbers on a Number Line

1 What are the missing numbers?

(a)

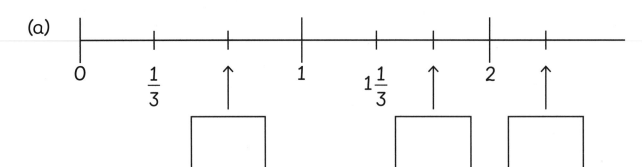

(b)

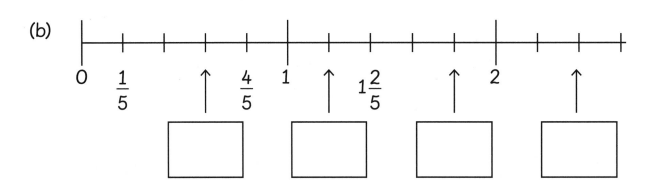

2 Show the following numbers on the number line.

(a) $1\frac{1}{2}$, $2\frac{3}{4}$, $2\frac{1}{2}$ and $1\frac{3}{4}$

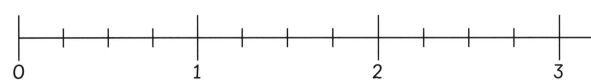

(b) $1\frac{1}{8}$, $2\frac{1}{8}$, $2\frac{3}{8}$ and $1\frac{5}{8}$

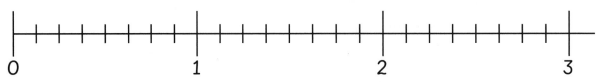

Name: _____ Class: _____ Date: _____

Worksheet 4

Finding Equivalent Fractions

1 Divide and shade the bars to show the equivalent fractions.
Fill in the blanks.

(a)

1

$\frac{1}{2}$	

$$\frac{1}{2} = \boxed{\frac{}{4}} = \boxed{\frac{3}{}}$$

(b)

1

$\frac{1}{5}$	$\frac{1}{5}$	$\frac{1}{5}$	$\frac{1}{5}$	

$$\frac{4}{5} = \boxed{\frac{}{10}} = \boxed{\frac{12}{}} = \boxed{\frac{}{20}}$$

2 Fill in the blanks.

(a) $\frac{1}{4} = \boxed{\dfrac{}{8}} = \boxed{\dfrac{3}{}}$

$\frac{2}{4} = \boxed{\dfrac{}{12}} = \boxed{\dfrac{1}{}}$

$\frac{3}{4} = \boxed{\dfrac{}{16}} = \boxed{\dfrac{15}{}}$

(b) $\frac{1}{6} = \boxed{\dfrac{}{12}} = \boxed{\dfrac{4}{}}$

$\frac{2}{6} = \boxed{\dfrac{}{3}} = \boxed{\dfrac{3}{}}$

$\frac{5}{6} = \boxed{\dfrac{}{18}} = \boxed{\dfrac{25}{}}$

(c) $\frac{1}{7} = \boxed{\dfrac{}{21}} = \boxed{\dfrac{2}{}}$

$\frac{3}{7} = \boxed{\dfrac{}{28}} = \boxed{\dfrac{9}{}}$

$\frac{6}{7} = \boxed{\dfrac{}{49}} = \boxed{\dfrac{30}{}}$

Worksheet 5

Finding Equivalent Fractions

1 Fill in the blanks.

(a) $\dfrac{1}{4} = \dfrac{}{60}$

 $\dfrac{2}{4} = \dfrac{}{60}$

 $\dfrac{3}{4} = \dfrac{}{60}$

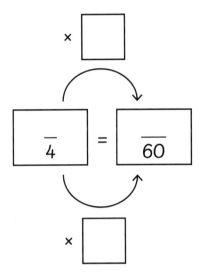

(b) $\dfrac{1}{10} = \dfrac{}{200}$

 $\dfrac{2}{10} = \dfrac{}{200}$

 $\dfrac{3}{10} = \dfrac{}{200}$

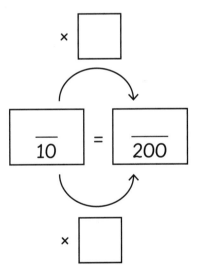

2 Fill in the blanks.

(a) $\dfrac{1}{8} = \dfrac{\quad}{40}$

   $\dfrac{3}{8} = \dfrac{\quad}{40}$

   $\dfrac{5}{8} = \dfrac{\quad}{40}$

   $\dfrac{7}{8} = \dfrac{\quad}{40}$

(b) $\dfrac{1}{9} = \dfrac{\quad}{99}$

   $\dfrac{4}{9} = \dfrac{\quad}{99}$

   $\dfrac{7}{9} = \dfrac{\quad}{99}$

   $\dfrac{8}{9} = \dfrac{\quad}{99}$

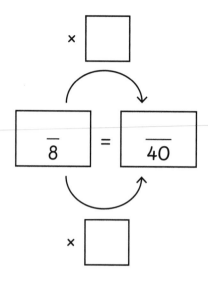

Worksheet 6

Simplifying Mixed Numbers

1 Simplify.

(a) $2\dfrac{4}{12} =$ ☐

(b) $3\dfrac{6}{10} =$ ☐

2 Write each mixed number in its simplest form.

(a) $2\dfrac{6}{8} =$ ☐

$\div$ ☐

$\dfrac{6}{8} = \dfrac{☐}{☐}$

$\div$ ☐

(b) $3\dfrac{8}{12} =$ ☐

$\div$ ☐

$\dfrac{8}{12} = \dfrac{☐}{☐}$

$\div$ ☐

(c) $4\dfrac{5}{20} = \boxed{}$

$\div \boxed{}$

$\dfrac{5}{20} = \dfrac{\boxed{}}{\boxed{}}$

$\div \boxed{}$

(d) $6\dfrac{6}{9} = \boxed{}$

$\div \boxed{}$

$\dfrac{6}{9} = \dfrac{\boxed{}}{\boxed{}}$

$\div \boxed{}$

3 Circle the mixed numbers that are in the simplest forms.

$2\dfrac{3}{5}$ $9\dfrac{4}{10}$ $1\dfrac{5}{8}$ $7\dfrac{4}{6}$

$3\dfrac{3}{9}$ $6\dfrac{2}{8}$ $2\dfrac{5}{12}$ $4\dfrac{3}{7}$

4 Match each mixed number with its simplest form.

$1\dfrac{8}{12}$ •   • $2\dfrac{1}{2}$

$2\dfrac{2}{4}$ •   • $2\dfrac{1}{4}$

$1\dfrac{3}{9}$ •   • $1\dfrac{2}{3}$

$2\dfrac{2}{8}$ •   • $2\dfrac{2}{3}$

$2\dfrac{4}{6}$ •   • $1\dfrac{1}{3}$

Name: _____ Class: _____ Date: _____

Worksheet 7

Simplifying Improper Fractions

1 Simplify.

(a) $\dfrac{15}{9}$ = [   ]

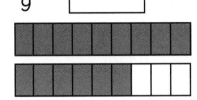

(b) $\dfrac{20}{6}$ = [   ]

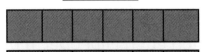

2 Write each improper fraction in its simplest form.

(a) $\dfrac{22}{10}$ = [   ]

$$\div\ [\ ]$$

$$\frac{22}{10} = \frac{[\ ]}{[\ ]}$$

$$\div\ [\ ]$$

(b) $\dfrac{30}{9}$ = [   ]

$$\div\ [\ ]$$

$$\frac{30}{9} = \frac{[\ ]}{[\ ]}$$

$$\div\ [\ ]$$

3 Circle the improper fractions that are in their simplest forms.

$\dfrac{12}{5}$	$\dfrac{15}{9}$	$\dfrac{27}{8}$	$\dfrac{15}{4}$
$\dfrac{33}{6}$	$\dfrac{22}{7}$	$\dfrac{15}{12}$	$\dfrac{24}{10}$

4 Match each improper fraction with its simplest form.

$\dfrac{14}{8}$ •   • $\dfrac{7}{3}$

$\dfrac{26}{6}$ •   • $\dfrac{7}{4}$

$\dfrac{18}{10}$ •   • $\dfrac{9}{5}$

$\dfrac{21}{9}$ •   • $\dfrac{13}{3}$

$\dfrac{30}{4}$ •   • $\dfrac{11}{6}$

$\dfrac{22}{12}$ •   • $\dfrac{15}{2}$

Name: _____ **Class:** _____ **Date:** _____

Worksheet 8

Adding Fractions

1 Fill in the blanks.

(a)

$\dfrac{2}{3}$ and $\dfrac{2}{3}$ make 1 and .

(b)

$\dfrac{3}{5}$ and $\dfrac{4}{5}$ make 1 and .

(c)
 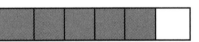

$\dfrac{2}{6}$ and $\dfrac{5}{6}$ make and .

(d)
 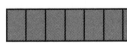

$\dfrac{5}{9}$ and $\dfrac{8}{9}$ make and .

Worksheet 9

Adding Fractions

1 Add.

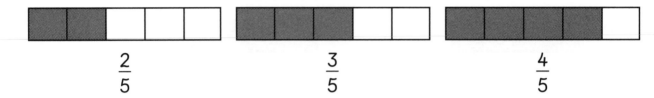

$$\frac{2}{5} \qquad \frac{3}{5} \qquad \frac{4}{5}$$

(a) $\frac{2}{5} + \frac{4}{5} =$ ⬚/5

= 1 + ⬚/5

= ⬚

(b) $\frac{2}{5} + \frac{3}{5} =$ ⬚/5

= ⬚

(c) $\frac{3}{5} + \frac{4}{5} =$ ⬚

= ⬚ + ⬚

= ⬚

2 Add.

(a) $\dfrac{2}{4} + \dfrac{3}{4} = \boxed{\dfrac{}{4}}$

(b) $\dfrac{8}{7} + \dfrac{5}{7} = \boxed{\dfrac{}{7}}$

(c) $\dfrac{4}{9} + \dfrac{7}{9} = \boxed{\dfrac{}{9}}$

(d) $\dfrac{5}{6} + \dfrac{2}{6} = 1 + \boxed{\dfrac{}{6}} = \boxed{}$

(e) $\dfrac{6}{8} + \dfrac{7}{8} = \boxed{} + \boxed{} = \boxed{}$

(f) $2\dfrac{3}{9} + \dfrac{7}{9} = 2 + \boxed{} = \boxed{}$

(g) $5\dfrac{4}{8} + \dfrac{11}{8} = 5 + \boxed{} = \boxed{}$

(h) $\dfrac{9}{10} + \dfrac{10}{10} = \boxed{\dfrac{}{10}} = \boxed{}$

(i) $\dfrac{4}{5} + \dfrac{4}{5} = 1 + \boxed{} = \boxed{}$

(j) $1\dfrac{3}{7} + \dfrac{6}{7} = 1 + \boxed{} = \boxed{}$

Worksheet 10

Adding Fractions

1 Add and then write each fraction in its simplest form.

$$\frac{4}{9} \qquad \frac{8}{9} \qquad \frac{7}{9}$$

(a) $\dfrac{4}{9} + \dfrac{8}{9} = \boxed{\dfrac{}{9}}$

$= 1 + \boxed{\dfrac{}{9}}$

$= \boxed{}$

(b) $\dfrac{8}{9} + \dfrac{7}{9} = \boxed{}$

$= \boxed{} + \boxed{}$

$= \boxed{} + \boxed{}$

$= \boxed{}$

(c) $\dfrac{4}{9} + \dfrac{8}{9} + \dfrac{7}{9} = \boxed{}$

$= \boxed{} + \boxed{} = \boxed{}$

2 Show your answers in the simplest form.

(a) $\dfrac{3}{4} + \dfrac{3}{4} = \boxed{\dfrac{}{4}} = \boxed{}$

(b) $\dfrac{7}{6} + \dfrac{3}{6} = \boxed{\dfrac{}{6}} = \boxed{}$

(c) $\dfrac{13}{12} + \dfrac{8}{12} = \boxed{\dfrac{}{12}} = \boxed{}$

(d) $\dfrac{7}{10} + \dfrac{9}{10} = \boxed{\dfrac{}{10}} = \boxed{}$

3 Add and then write each answer its simplest form.

(a) $\dfrac{5}{6} + \dfrac{3}{6} = 1 + \boxed{\dfrac{}{6}} = \boxed{}$

(b) $\dfrac{5}{8} + \dfrac{7}{8} = \boxed{} + \boxed{} = \boxed{}$

(c) $2\dfrac{9}{10} + \dfrac{6}{10} = \boxed{} + \boxed{}$

$= \boxed{} + \boxed{} = \boxed{}$

(d) $\dfrac{3}{4} + \dfrac{3}{4} + \dfrac{4}{4} = \boxed{} + \boxed{} = \boxed{}$

Worksheet 11

Subtracting Fractions

1 Subtract and fill in the blanks.

(a) $2 - \dfrac{1}{6} = \boxed{1\dfrac{6}{6}} - \boxed{\dfrac{1}{6}} = \boxed{}$

(b) $3 - \dfrac{2}{5} = \boxed{} - \boxed{} = \boxed{}$

(c) $5 - \dfrac{1}{3} = \boxed{} - \boxed{} = \boxed{}$

2 finds the difference between 3 and $\dfrac{1}{2}$ like this.

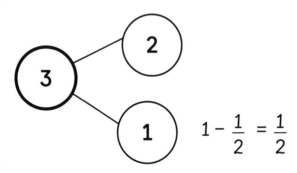

$1 - \dfrac{1}{2} = \dfrac{1}{2}$

$3 - \dfrac{1}{2} = 2 + \dfrac{1}{2} = 2\dfrac{1}{2}$

Subtract, using 's method.

(a) $4 - \dfrac{4}{7} =$ ☐ $+$ ☐ $=$ ☐

(b) $5 - \dfrac{3}{8} =$ ☐ $+$ ☐ $=$ ☐

(c) $6 - \dfrac{5}{9} =$ ☐ $+$ ☐ $=$ ☐

3 Subtract and give each answer in its simplest form.

(a) $2 - \dfrac{2}{10} =$ $\boxed{1\dfrac{10}{10}}$ $-$ $\boxed{\dfrac{2}{10}}$ $=$ ☐ $=$ ☐

(b) $4 - \dfrac{4}{6} =$ ☐ $-$ ☐ $=$ ☐ $=$ ☐

(c) $3 - \dfrac{2}{8} =$ ☐ $-$ ☐ $=$ ☐ $=$ ☐

(d) $9 - \dfrac{8}{12} =$ ☐ $-$ ☐ $=$ ☐ $=$ ☐

(e) $5 - \dfrac{2}{4} =$ ☐ $-$ ☐ $=$ ☐ $=$ ☐

(f) $6 - \dfrac{6}{9} =$ ☐ $-$ ☐ $=$ ☐ $=$ ☐

Worksheet 12

Subtracting Fractions

1 Subtract and fill in the blanks.

(a) $1\frac{1}{3} - \frac{2}{3} = \boxed{\dfrac{4}{3}} - \boxed{\dfrac{2}{3}} = \boxed{}$

(b) $1\frac{5}{8} - \frac{6}{8} = \boxed{} - \boxed{} = \boxed{}$

(c) $2\frac{2}{5} - \frac{3}{5} = \boxed{} - \boxed{} = \boxed{}$

2 Subtract and then write each answer in its simplest form.

(a) $1\frac{3}{6} - \frac{5}{6} = \boxed{} - \boxed{} = \boxed{} = \boxed{}$

(b) $1\frac{1}{4} - \frac{3}{4} = \boxed{} - \boxed{} = \boxed{} = \boxed{}$

(c) $1\frac{7}{10} - \frac{9}{10} = \boxed{} - \boxed{} = \boxed{} = \boxed{}$

(d) $2\frac{4}{9} - \frac{7}{9} = \boxed{} - \boxed{} = \boxed{} = \boxed{}$

3 This is how finds the difference between $1\frac{1}{3}$ and $\frac{2}{3}$.

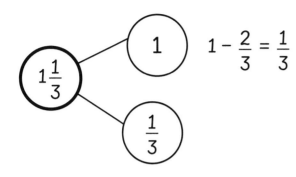 $1 - \frac{2}{3} = \frac{1}{3}$

$1\frac{1}{3} - \frac{2}{3} = \frac{1}{3} + \frac{1}{3} = \frac{2}{3}$

Subtract, using 's method.

(a) $1\frac{2}{4} - \frac{3}{4} = \boxed{\frac{2}{4}} + \boxed{\frac{1}{4}} = \boxed{}$

(b) $1\frac{2}{5} - \frac{4}{5} = \boxed{} + \boxed{} = \boxed{}$

(c) $1\frac{1}{6} - \frac{4}{6} = \boxed{} + \boxed{} = \boxed{} = \boxed{}$

(d) $2\frac{2}{9} - \frac{8}{9} = \boxed{} + \boxed{} = \boxed{} = \boxed{}$

(e) $3\frac{3}{10} - \frac{7}{10} = \boxed{} + \boxed{} = \boxed{} = \boxed{}$

Worksheet 13

Solving Word Problems

1 Charles cuts a 5-m ribbon into pieces, each $\frac{1}{4}$ m long.

How many pieces does he get?

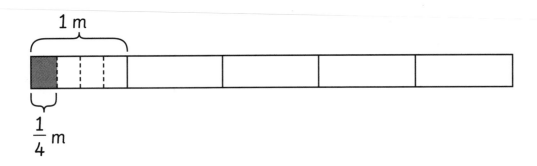

He gets [   ] $\frac{1}{4}$ m long pieces of ribbon.

2 A small bottle can hold $\frac{2}{5}$ l of water.

A container holds 6 l of water.
How many small bottles of water will fill the container completely?

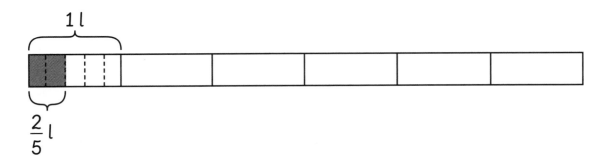

[   ] small bottles of water will fill the container completely.

3 Holly had 3 kg of flour.

She used $\frac{3}{4}$ kg of flour to bake buns and the rest

to bake cookies.

Each cookie needs $\frac{1}{8}$ kg of flour.

How many cookies did Holly bake?

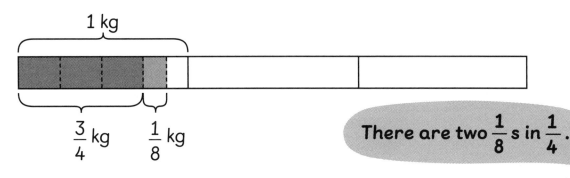

1 kg

$\frac{3}{4}$ kg $\frac{1}{8}$ kg

There are two $\frac{1}{8}$ s in $\frac{1}{4}$.

4 Lulu had 1 l of water in her bottle at first.

She then drank $\frac{4}{10}$ l during break, and added $\frac{7}{10}$ l more water to her

bottle from the tap.

Find the volume of water Lulu had in her bottle in the end.

Date: _____

The mass of an empty container is $\frac{3}{10}$ kg.

When the container is half filled with water, the mass becomes $1\frac{1}{10}$ kg.

What is the mass of the container when it is completely filled with water?

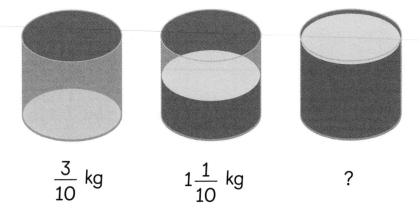

$\frac{3}{10}$ kg $1\frac{1}{10}$ kg   ?

Review 6

1 What are the missing numbers?

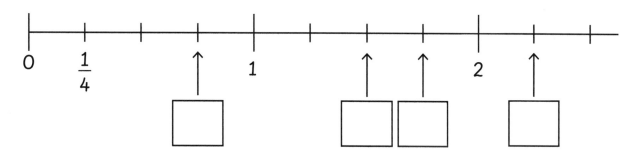

2 Show the following numbers on the number line.

$1\frac{1}{3}$, $2\frac{1}{6}$, $2\frac{5}{6}$ and $\frac{2}{3}$

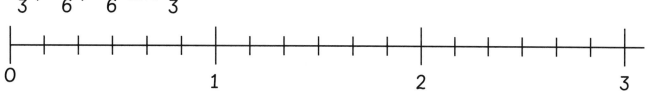

3 Complete the equivalent fractions.

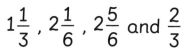

$\frac{1}{10}$ = $\dfrac{}{20}$ = $\dfrac{5}{}$ = $\dfrac{10}{}$

$\frac{6}{10}$ = $\dfrac{}{20}$ = $\dfrac{3}{}$ = $\dfrac{36}{}$

$\frac{9}{10}$ = $\dfrac{}{40}$ = $\dfrac{54}{}$ = $\dfrac{45}{}$

4 Add and give each answer in its simplest form.

(a) $\dfrac{3}{7} + \dfrac{6}{7} =$ ☐ $+$ ☐ $=$ ☐

(b) $1\dfrac{3}{8} + \dfrac{7}{8} =$ ☐ $+$ ☐ $=$ ☐ $=$ ☐

5 Subtract and give each answer in its simplest form.

(a) $6 - \dfrac{3}{5} =$ ☐ $-$ ☐ $=$ ☐

(b) $2\dfrac{3}{9} - \dfrac{8}{9} =$ ☐ $-$ ☐ $=$ ☐

6 Ruby needs 3 kg of sugar.

Sugar is sold in packets of $\dfrac{1}{5}$ kg each.

How many $\dfrac{1}{5}$ kg packets should she buy altogether?

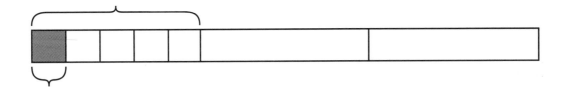

Time

Name: _____ Class: _____ Date: _____

Worksheet 1

Telling Time on a 24-Hour Clock

1 Match.

6:30pm ●	● 12:00
10:15am ●	● 06:30
6:30am ●	● 10:15
12:00am ●	● 03:50
3:50pm ●	● 15:50
12:00pm ●	● 18:30
3:50am ●	● 22:15
10:15pm ●	● 00:00

2 The table shows the train schedule between Town A and Town B.

Departure time from Town A to Town B	Departure time from Town B to Town A
8:15 a.m.	10:30 a.m.
11:45 a.m.	1:00 p.m.
3:00 p.m.	4:15 p.m.
5:30 p.m.	7:00 p.m.

(a) Using the 24-hour clock, write the departure times for the trains listed below.

From Town A to Town B		From Town B to Town A	
First train	Last train	First train	Last train

(b) The departure time printed on Lulu's ticket is 13:00.

Lulu is travelling from Town ☐ to Town ☐ .

(c) Elliott is visiting a museum in Town B.
He plans to leave the museum at 15:00 and take the earliest train back to Town A.
If Elliott takes 20 min to walk from the museum to the train station, what is the departure time of the train that he should book?
Write your answer using the 24-hour clock.

☐

Worksheet 2

Changing Time in Minutes to Seconds

1 Fill in the blanks.

(a) 3 minutes = [ ] seconds

(b) 5 minutes = [ ] seconds

(c) 10 minutes = [ ] seconds

(d) 60 minutes = [ ] seconds

(f) 120 minutes = [ ] seconds

(f) 150 minutes = [ ] seconds

(g) 1 minute 15 seconds = [ ] seconds

(h) 2 minutes 50 seconds = [ ] seconds

2 Emma takes 2 minutes to walk to the park from her home.
She takes 3 minutes to walk home from the park.
How many seconds does Emma take to walk to the park and back home again?

Worksheet 3

Changing Time in Hours to Minutes

1 Fill in the blanks.

(a) 1 h = 60 min

2 h = [ ] min

3 h = [ ] min

5 h = [ ] min

(b) 1 h = 60 min

$\frac{1}{2}$ h = [ ] min

$1\frac{1}{2}$ h = [ ] min

$2\frac{1}{2}$ h = [ ] min

2 How many minutes have passed?

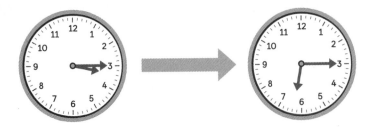

[ ] minutes have passed.

3 Ravi took 2 h 36 min to complete his assignment.
How many minutes did Ravi take to complete his assignment?

4 Match.

1 hour 30 minutes ●	● 130 minutes
2 hours 10 minutes ●	● 110 minutes
1 hour 50 minutes ●	● 90 minutes
2 hours 20 minutes ●	● 140 minutes

Worksheet 4

Solving Problems on Duration of Time

Solve.

1 A bus takes 2 h 20 min to travel from Town A to Town B.
The bus left Town A at 10:40.
At what time will the bus arrive at Town B?

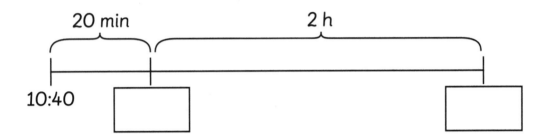

The bus will arrive at Town B at ⬚ .

2 The same bus takes 3 h 5 min to return to Town A from Town B.
The bus reached Town A at 17:45.
At what time did the bus leave from Town B?

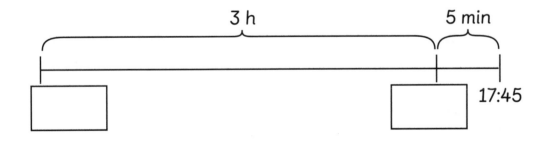

The bus left Town B at ⬚ .

3 Ruby arrived at the library at 11:50.
She left the library at 14:05.
How long did she spend at the library?

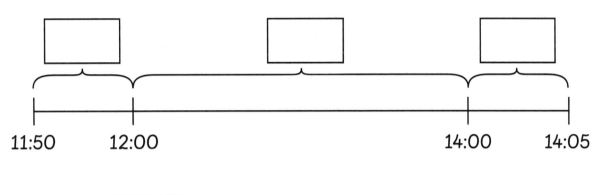

11:50   12:00   14:00   14:05

She spent ⬚ at the library.

4 Charles watched a late night show that began at 23:15 on Saturday.
The show lasted for 2 h 30 min.
When did the show end?

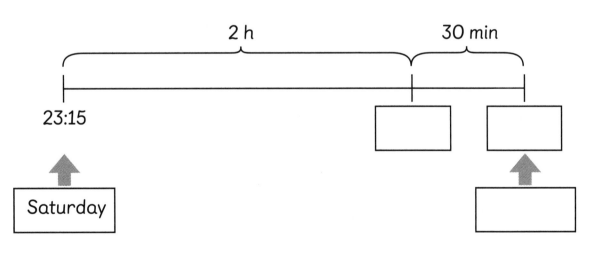

2 h   30 min

23:15

Saturday

The show ended at ⬚ on ⬚ .

Name: _____   Class: _____   Date: _____

Worksheet 5

Changing Years to Months and Weeks to Days

1 grew a tree from a seedling.
She recorded the growth of the tree.

Height	Time taken
1 m	1 year
2 m	1 year 6 months
5 m	3 years
10 m	5 years

(a)   It took 1 year and 6 months for the tree to grow to 2 m.

1 year 6 months = ☐ months + ☐ months

= ☐ months

(b)   The tree took 3 years to grow to 5 m.

3 years = ☐ × ☐ months

= ☐ months

(c)   How many months did the tree take to grow to 10 m?

5 years = ☐ × ☐ months

= ☐ months

2 Holly, Amira and Lulu read *The Chronicles of Narnia* during the school holiday.

I took 2 weeks to read the book.

It took me 3 weeks and 4 days to read the book.

I took 5 weeks to finish reading the book.

Holly

Lulu

Amira

(a) How many days did Holly take to finish reading the book?

1 week = 7 days

2 weeks = [ ] × [ ] days = [ ] days

(b) How many days did Lulu take to finish reading the book?

3 weeks 4 days = [ ] days + [ ] days

= [ ] days

(c) How many days did Amira take to finish reading the book?

5 weeks = [ ] × [ ] days = [ ] days

Worksheet 6

Solving Word Problems

Solve.

1 Charles left Town X for Town Z at 11:30.

He travelled for 3 h 15 min before arriving at Town Y.

Then he continued his journey and arrived at Town Z at 18:05.

How long did his journey from Town Y to Town Z take?

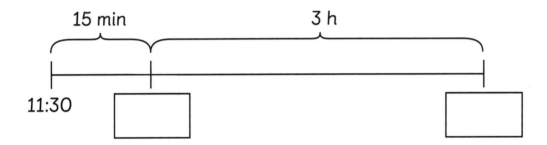

He arrived at Town Y at ⬜ .

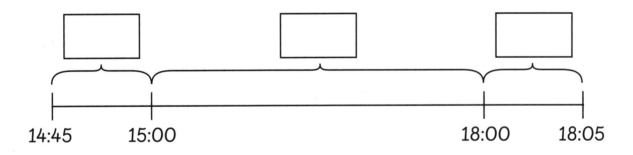

Charles' journey from Town Y to Town Z took ⬜ .

2 Emma started gardening at 10:20.
She took 1 h 50 min to clear out the weeds and another 3 h 25 min planting the flower and vegetable seeds.
At what time did Emma finish gardening?

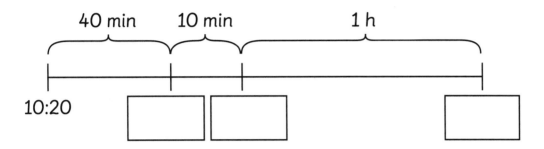

40 min   10 min   1 h

10:20

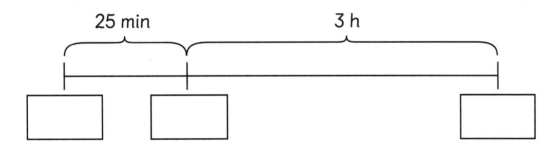

25 min   3 h

Emma finished gardening at ⬚.

Date: _____

An old clock loses 5 minutes every hour.
At noon, the clock was adjusted to the correct time.
What time will the clock show 6 hours later?

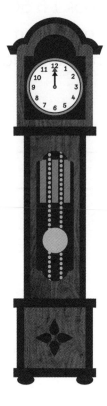

Name: _____ Class: _____ Date: _____

Review 7

1 Fill in the blanks.

(a) 5 minutes = [　　　] seconds

(b) 10 minutes 15 seconds = [　　　] seconds

(c) 4 hours = [　　　] minutes

(d) $\frac{1}{2}$ hour = [　　　] minutes

(e) 6 hours 10 minutes = [　　　] minutes

Solve.

2 Hannah started her piano lesson at 09:55.
Her lesson ended at 12:05.
How long was her piano lesson?

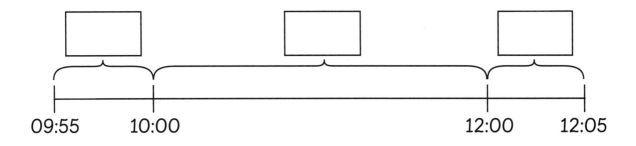

09:55   10:00   12:00   12:05

Her piano lesson was [　　　] long.

3 Ravi started painting a wall at 08:35.
He spent 3 h 45 min painting before taking a break.
He continued painting again at 13:50.
How long was Ravi's break?

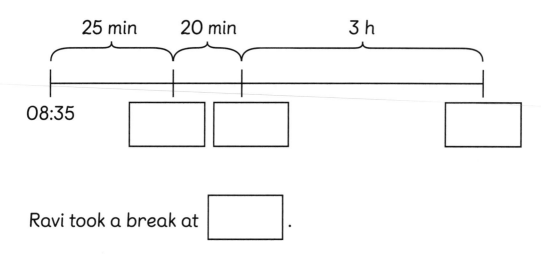

08:35

Ravi took a break at ▢ .

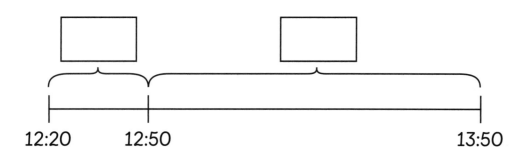

12:20   12:50   13:50

Ravi's break was ▢ long.

Name: _____ Class: _____ Date: _____

Revision 2

1 The line graph shows the price of ferry tickets in different years.

Price of Ferry Ticket

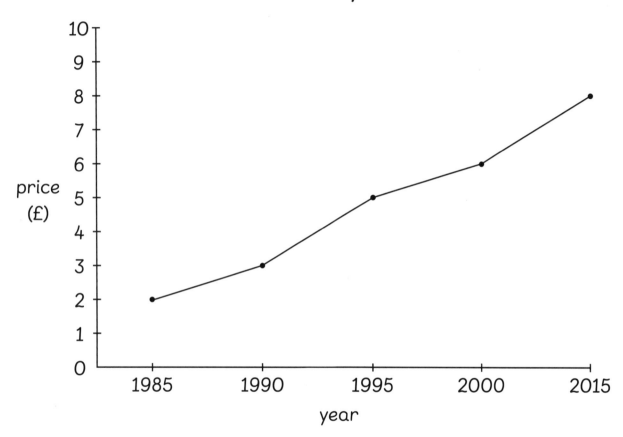

(a) What is the price of a ferry ticket in 1995?

(b) What is the difference in the price of a ferry ticket in 1985 and 2015?

(c) There is an error in the layout of the line graph. What is the error?

2 Cross out the mixed numbers that are not in their simplest forms.

$3\frac{4}{6}$ $2\frac{5}{9}$ $1\frac{5}{10}$ $1\frac{7}{12}$

3 Cross out the improper fractions that are not in their simplest forms.

$\frac{33}{12}$ $\frac{16}{3}$ $\frac{12}{5}$ $\frac{25}{10}$

4 Complete the equivalent fractions.

(a) $\frac{1}{5} = \frac{}{15} = \frac{5}{} = \frac{9}{}$

(b) $\frac{4}{7} = \frac{}{42} = \frac{}{35} = \frac{36}{}$

(c) $\frac{6}{12} = \frac{1}{2} = \frac{4}{} = \frac{11}{}$

(d) $\frac{2}{3} = \frac{}{21} = \frac{12}{} = \frac{}{27}$

5 Add and then write each answer in its simplest form.

(a) $\dfrac{5}{6} + \dfrac{2}{6} =$ ☐ $+$ ☐ $=$ ☐

(b) $2\dfrac{7}{10} + \dfrac{9}{10} =$ ☐ $+$ ☐ $=$ ☐ $=$ ☐

6 Subtract and then write each answer in its simplest form.

(a) $3 - \dfrac{3}{4} =$ ☐ $-$ ☐ $=$ ☐

(b) $4\dfrac{2}{7} - \dfrac{6}{7} =$ ☐ $-$ ☐ $=$ ☐

7 Fill in the blanks.

(a) 6 minutes = ☐ seconds

(b) 11 minutes 20 seconds = ☐ seconds

(c) 12 hours = ☐ minutes

(d) 5 hours 50 minutes = ☐ minutes

(e) 3 years = ☐ months

(f) 9 weeks = ☐ days

Solve.

8 Lulu bought 2 kg of sugar.

She used $\frac{1}{2}$ kg of sugar to make pudding and then she put

the rest into $\frac{1}{4}$ kg packets.

How many $\frac{1}{4}$ kg packets did she get?

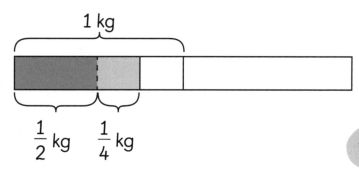

1 kg

$\frac{1}{2}$ kg $\frac{1}{4}$ kg

There are two $\frac{1}{4}$ s in $\frac{1}{2}$.

9 Emma had 1 l of orange juice in a jug.

She used $\frac{1}{6}$ l of the orange juice to make some fruit punch.

She then added $\frac{5}{6}$ l of orange juice into the jug.

How many litres of orange juice did she have in the end?

10 Sam boarded the train at 22:30 on Sunday.
The journey was 5 h 30 min.
When did Sam arrive at his destination?

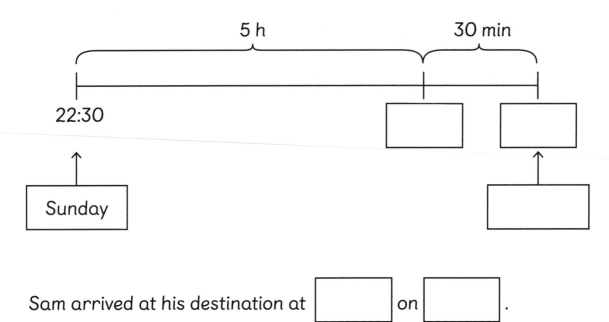

Sam arrived at his destination at [   ] on [   ] .

Name: _____ Class: _____ Date: _____

Mid-Year Revision

Section A
Choose the correct answer.
Write its matching number – (1), (2), (3) or (4) – in the box.

1 What is 5000 + 80 + 2 + 400?
- (1) 5428
- (2) 5842
- (3) 5482
- (4) 5824

( )

2 In 9183, what is the value of the digit 9?
- (1) 9 ones
- (2) 9 hundreds
- (3) 90 tens
- (4) 90 hundreds

( )

3 Study the number pattern.

8756, 8846, 8936, ⬜ , 9116

What is the missing number?
- (1) 8926
- (2) 9026
- (3) 9036
- (4) 9126

( )

4 Find the difference between the masses of the two pieces of fruit.

watermelon
2428 g

papaya
878 g

(1)   1550 g

(2)   2450 g

(3)   2550 g

(4)   3306 g

(   )

5 3599 is 111 more than ☐ .

(1)   2488

(2)   3488

(3)   3710

(4)   4710

(   )

6 Which of the following is not an equivalent fraction of $\frac{3}{4}$?

(1) $\frac{6}{8}$

(2) $\frac{9}{12}$

(3) $\frac{15}{20}$

(4) $\frac{20}{24}$

(   )

7 How many minutes are there in $2\frac{1}{2}$ h?

(1)   25

(2)   125

(3)   150

(4)   250

(   )

8 Ravi wants to put 100 marbles into small containers.
Each container can hold 8 marbles.
At least how many containers will Ravi need?

(1)   13

(2)   12

(3)   8

(4)   4

(   )

9 A television costs £1299. It costs £500 less than a refrigerator.
What is the total cost of a television and a refrigerator?

(1)   £799

(2)   £1799

(3)   £2098

(4)   £3098

(   )

10 Which of the following is not in its simplest form?

(1) $1\frac{3}{12}$

(2) $2\frac{5}{12}$

(3) $1\frac{2}{11}$

(4) $3\frac{8}{15}$

(   )

Section B

Write your answers in the spaces provided.

11 Write 7846 in words.

12 Arrange the numbers from greatest to smallest.

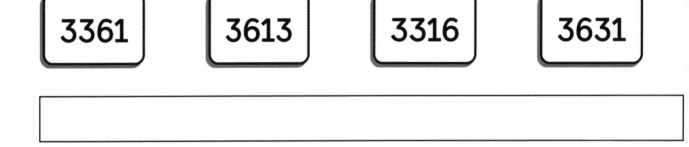

| 3361 | 3613 | 3316 | 3631 |

13 1000 more than 3650 is the same as 100 less than 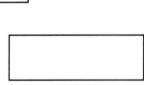 ? .

What is the missing number?

14 Form the smallest 4-digit even number using these four digits.

| 8 | 5 | 6 | 3 |

15 Round 7099 to the nearest 1000.

16 What is the missing digit?

```
    8   6   0   8
-   3   5  [?]  9
_____
    5   0   3   9
_____
```

17 $\frac{2}{9}$ and [?] make 1.

What is the missing fraction?

18 How long is a movie that starts at 11:25 and ends at 14:05?

h   min

19 What is the missing number?

$15 \times 11 = $ [?] $\times 11 + 7 \times 11$

20 How many minutes have passed?

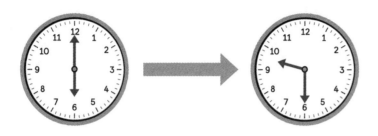

	min

21 Amira had 89 sweets and she shared them equally with her friends.
Each person got 9 sweets and 8 sweets were left over.
With how many friends did Amira share her sweets?

22 Multiply.

```
    6   8   5
 ×          9
_____
```

23 What is the difference between 50 hundreds and 50 tens?

24 $2\dfrac{1}{5} - \dfrac{4}{5} = \boxed{\quad ? \quad}$

Show your answer as a mixed number.

25 Ruby has 6 different hats and 4 different bags.
How many different combinations can she create?

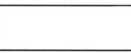

26 Charles joined two paper chains together.
The longer chain was $1\dfrac{2}{5}$ m long, while the shorter one was $\dfrac{4}{5}$ m long.
What was the total length of the paper chain once the two pieces were joined together?

$\boxed{\qquad\qquad\qquad \text{m}}$

27 A plane departed from Gatwick airport at 18:50 and flew for 6 h 30 min.
At what time did the plane arrive at its destination?

$\boxed{\qquad\qquad\qquad}$

28 How much would you pay for 8 kg of grapes and 7 kg of mangoes?

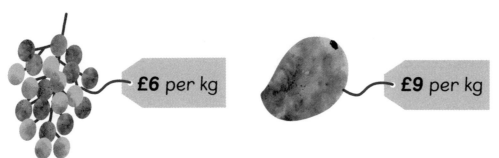

£6 per kg   **£9** per kg

£ ____

29 The total mass of a box and a parcel is 280 g.

The box is 6 times as heavy as the parcel.

What is the mass of the box?

____ g

30 What number goes in the box?

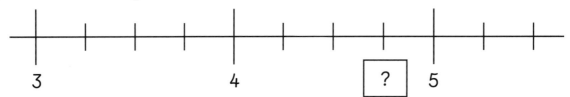

3   4   ?   5

____

31 How many months are there in 2 years and 3 months?

____ months

32 A number when rounded off to the nearest 100 is 4800.

What is the greatest possible value of the number?

33 After school, Ruby walked to the library.

From the library, she had to walk past the school to get home.

How far did she walk in total?

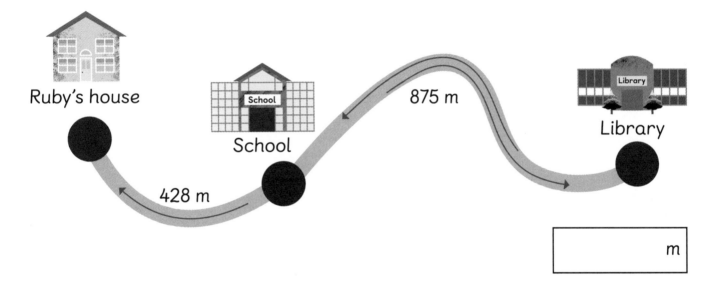

Ruby's house

School

School

875 m

Library

Library

428 m

m

34 Holly has £60. What is the largest number of doughnuts she can buy?

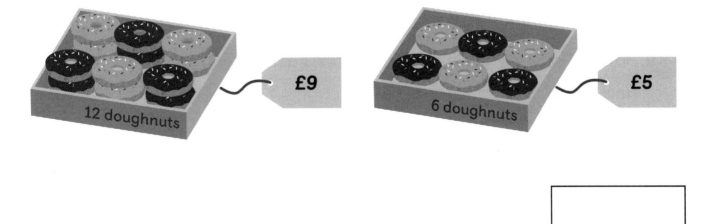

£9

12 doughnuts

£5

6 doughnuts

35 What is the remainder when 901 is divided by 8?

36 Charles had 3895 ml of water in his fish bowl.
He poured out 1358 ml and then added another 2524 ml of water to the bowl.
How much water is in the fish bowl now?

ml

37 There are 8765 people at a carnival. 5986 of them are children.
How many more children than adults are there?

38 Hannah cuts a 6-m ribbon into pieces, each $\frac{3}{5}$ m long.
How many pieces does she get?

39 Study the line graph below and answer question (a) and (b).

The graph shows the price of a tray of eggs in different years in one country.

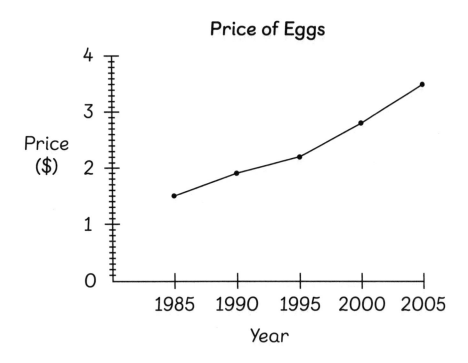

(a)   What is the difference between the price of a tray of eggs in 1995 and 2005?

$ [   ]

(b)   Did the price of a tray increase or decrease between 1990 and 2000? How much was the increase or decrease?

$ [   ]

40 There are 14 bicycles and 21 cars in a car park.

How many wheels are there altogether?

[   ]

Section C
Solve the word problems.
Show your work clearly.

41 There were 2497 visitors during the morning session at the zoo.
There were 1368 more visitors who came to the morning session than came to the afternoon session.
How many visitors were there altogether during the day?

42 Emma filled 8 bottles with equal amounts, using a mixture of blue- and green-coloured sand.
She had 360 g of blue-coloured sand and 200 g more green- than blue-coloured sand.
What was the mass of sand in each bottle?

43 Elliott had 638 fewer marbles than Ravi had.
Ravi then gave 352 marbles to Elliott.
Who had more marbles in the end? How many more?

44 There are 8 times as many pears as oranges in some baskets.
There are 612 pieces of fruit altogether.
How many more pears than oranges are there in the baskets?

45 Lulu bought 1 kg of flour.

Amira bought $\dfrac{3}{10}$ kg less flour than Lulu bought.

Holly bought twice as much flour as Amira bought.

How many kilograms of flour did the three girls buy altogether?